WHAT'S WRONG WITH MY WILLY?

WHAT'S WRONG WITH MY WILLY?

RAY HAMBLE

First published in August 1991
by GMP Publishers Ltd
P O Box 247, London N17 9QR, England

© 1991 Ray Hamble

A CIP catalogue record for this book
is available from the British LIbrary

ISBN 0 85449 166 X

Distributed in North America by InBook
140 Commerce Street, East Haven, CT 06512, USA

Distributed in Australia by Bulldog Books
P O Box 155, Broadway, NSW 2007, Australia

Printed and bound in the EC on environmentally-friendly paper
by Nørhaven A/S, Viborg, Denmark

INTRODUCTION

It was 1975 when I first came across Dr. Ray Hamble. He was then writing in the old *Him Exclusive* magazine. Since those days, Ray has turned into an institution. From the brief factual replies he gave many years ago, he has gradually turned into the Marje Proops of the gay world.

It is hard enough for some people to come to terms with the fact that they're gay. If you suddenly find you have a worrying medical problem, and you don't want your family doctor to know you're gay, then there aren't many people you can turn to. So Ray's been there like a knight in shining armour. Especially when he takes time out to personally reply to all the letters he receives. He has gathered around him quite a substantial fan club, and I can honestly say that I am one of his biggest fans.

Over the last few years I have got to know Ray well. He is a likeable, jolly man, who has the patience to listen. He is a splendid guest at dinner parties, where he can dispense advice like a kindly uncle. I'm pleased at long last that Ray has managed to put together some of the many letters he's received and, like me, hope that when you've read this, you'll be ready for Volume Two!

Brian Derbyshire,
June 1991

1

CALLING RAY HAMBLE

Calling Ray Hamble... Calling Ray Hamble... Are you receiving me? Over...

As always, when I write to you, a certain stirring occurs between my thighs. Do you feel a power over all the guys who write to you, knowing they've all probably got stiff dicks as they put pen to paper?

Wanker 5 (London)

Wanker 5.... Wanker 5.... Receiving you loud and clear.

No, I don't feel a sense of power over the folk who write to me but, let's face it, a few stiff dicks here and there are an important part of the Ray Hamble column. A bit of a laugh, a bit of a turn on, a modicum of health education, help with real gay sexual and relationship problems and the odd bizarre or kinky revelation — that's what it's all about.

●●●

I'm excited. This is my first book and I hope that you, my reader, will enjoy being with me as the pages unfold. After all, this is essentially a readers' book. Without all the letters I've received during the years I've been writing for HIM Magazine there wouldn't be a *What's Wrong With My Willy?* Hundreds upon hundreds of letters have arrived on my desk during the past four years. Some have been sad, or worried, or bizarre, or angry, or grateful, or funny, or — well you name it, almost every aspect of gay sex has had an airing. I like to think that nobody has been left wanting for a reply, though I'm just an ordinary doctor and I claim no more expertise than commonsense — the rarest of them all.

It isn't always easy to be gay. It has given rise to so many problems, and caused so many heartaches, that jingoistic phrases like 'Glad to be Gay' and 'Gay Pride' ring uncomfortably in the ears. Indeed for many gayness is the greatest of all misnomers. These are the men (and occasionally the women) for whom my monthly column and personal replies have offered a unique supportive leaning post. From nearly two hundred letters each month I select just six to eight for publication and from those I have, in turn, chosen the contents of this book.

I have tried to deal with as wide a range of topics as possible and, where appropriate, I've brought groups of letters relating to the same issue together. Many of my replies have been rewritten to take into account up to date information and to avoid repetition. But this isn't the definitive encyclopaedia of gay sex. It only answers the questions readers have raised. If you have a pet problem, or if there are other things you want to know, then why not write to me at the address at the end of this book and I'll do my best to come up with the answer.

I am often asked whether all the letters are genuine or whether I make them up myself. For anyone to credit me with such a vivid imagination is, I suppose, praise indeed. I can only say that what you read is as honest as its writer cares to make it. You may boggle at the things folk claim they do, and you won't be alone because I often feel the same. However, like me, you have no option but to accept what is before you at its face value. To be sure the world of gay sex is an odd one — and the oddities certainly seem to come my way.

I suppose I should admit that there have been occasions when I have had to edit and judiciously prune some of the longer letters to a more manageable length, and I have often helped my correspondents with some of the finer points of English grammar.

One of my most interesting letters, years ago, was 130 closely written pages of A4 manuscript. Oh, the frustration of arriving at the last page and being deprived of the chance to reply by the realisation that it was completely anonymous and far too long to print!

But anonymity isn't really necessary. I never print a letter without changing both the name and location of the writer to avoid even the slightest chance of unanticipated embarrassment. Even the staff at the HIM office are unaware of the real identity of those who confide in me because they only see the final retyped version ready for the printers. I have never kept any files, and I destroy all my incoming mail as soon as my reply has been prepared.

I say all this to reassure those of you who read this book, and those of you who recognise that you have inadvertently contributed to it when you see your letter in print, that identities have been preserved and the confidences of individuals have not been breached. If you actually happen to be a 'John' of 'Brighton' and you see a letter so attributed, let me emphasise that it really isn't you!

Sadly, some of the funniest letters have had to be omitted. By all means let us all share a laugh with my correpondents, but it would be unkind for us to laugh at them.

Take 'Kevin', for example, from 'Slough' — he used to write to me twice a week for many more years than HIM has been on the bookshop shelves. Often his letters would run to fifteen pages but I was rarely any the wiser after reading them than at the outset. That he was schizophrenic came across so clearly, but there was nothing I could do by post to alleviate the problems caused by the demons and hobgoblins which inhabited his balls and shouted their obscene (but incredibly funny) messages through his arse.

'Andy' also raised a smile when he described being held in bondage by a lover's penis so long that it entwined around his ankles. The trouble was that he totally believed in his fantasy.

Such tales are from the past and can be mentioned only because, alas, those involved are no longer with us, but even today equally strange folk take the stage from time to time. Theirs are the letters I would not care to print. They intrude too much on the individual's private life, or torment, and have to remain forever discreetly under wraps.

What else am I supposed to say in this introduction? Well, I guess I ought to include a word or two about myself. I'm not going to bore you with all my growing up snapshots or anything like that, but I have to refer briefly to my pedigree just to keep the record straight.

I am not a private person, in that I am not afraid to talk about myself, and much about my lifestyle will emerge from the pages which lie ahead. Indeed, it is because I am open and often all too ready to confess my homosexual 'sins' that I hide behind my Ray Hamble pseudonym. It would have been impossible to combine my career and my gay life under my real name. I know that maintaining my anonymity has incurred the wrath of many a gay political activist but, as a Gemini, I chose to lead the double life ascribed to me by the stars, and I have no intention of changing now that I have reached the age of fifty-eight.

I'd prefer not to have a 'political' voice in the gay community. That would mean taking sides and my whole aim is to remain neutral. Yes, of course, I'm concerned at the apparent injustice of the age of consent for gay men being a ridiculous twenty-one years, and, sure, I believe that some form of 'life contract' akin to heterosexual marriage should be a legal option, but I'm not the banner-waving, marching kind.

I come back to the point I've made before — I'm an ordinary man. I have no aspirations whatsoever to obtain notoriety as some sort of gay celebrity.

I have always perceived myself as being 100 per cent gay in spite of having been happily married for the best part of thirty years. From my first gay experience at the tender age of nine I have always set out to enjoy my sexuality. There's no point in feeling guilty or ashamed about it. I accept myself and have learned to live with my gayness with neither embarrassment nor guilt. I only live once so I might as well enjoy myself.

I am a sexual animal, not at all nice to know when I haven't had my rocks off for twenty-four hours or more. I can't concentrate, I become irritable and depressed and physically I feel more and more uncomfortable in those anatomical parts to which only the best of lagers penetrate. Those anatomical parts, by the way, aren't destined to set the world on fire. I'll never be worthy of a photograph in HIM. Perhaps it's because I'm just average that I feel a bit intimidated when a big boy comes along.

My liking for the smaller man (five inches or less) borders upon a fetish, though, from a distance, I can admire the ten inch stallion and raise the proverbial eyebrow. I'm very broad-minded in that I'm mightily turned on by an older guy with a bit of beam and bust — but I'd be dishonest if I didn't agree that a slim and attractive chicken has his charm.

Am I allowed to have a fetish? Why not? OK, I'll tell you about two of them. I love the smooth, clean feel of a closely shaved pubic area and for years have paid as much attention down there as to my chin. Oh, and the other one — spunk. Isn't it just the most magical liquid in the world? But I'll spare you the gory details.

Gayness has been much more than my sexuality over the years. It has been my hobby too. Quite apart from the physical thrills of being a twice-a-day wanker for almost fifty years and with a list of partners which reads like a roll of honour, I'm fascinated by the whole subject of homosexuality. Why are some folk gay? I dunno! What makes gay men tick? I dunno that either! What a wonderful variety there exists when it comes to gay sexual techniques and the gay scene across the world. The whole subject is simply packed with interest and it never bores me — even when I haven't got a hard on!

As for my marriage, it has offered me companionship, support when things have been low and, I suppose, the key to an enjoyable professional social life which would otherwise have been difficult. The relationship with my wife is most certainly not without love — a very deep and real love — though, thankfully, sex is something we have avoided by mutual consent for over twenty-five years.

Looking back, I find it hard to believe that I have been a doctor for more than thirty-five years. Quite early on in my career I opted for the administrative side of my profession and that speciality which has been known variously as public health or community medicine. As an NHS consultant in this field I don't have individual patients in the accepted sense but deal instead with disease as it affects the community as a whole. For instance my work nowadays is almost entirely devoted to controlling the spread of AIDS through health education and the promotion of safer sex and warning of the dangers of injecting illicit drugs using infected 'works'.

The publication of this book marks two decades of writing for the gay press for I was at it long before the new HIM re-emerged like a phoenix over four years ago. My agony column has a long history going back to the early seventies when I began writing in a magazine called *Quorum* edited by Roger Baker. Since then I've been passed from publisher's pillar to post — *Man to Man, IF, Manifique, Zipper, Mister*, Old Uncle Tom Cobbleigh and All.

I have confined myself in this book only to letters which have appeared in HIM. I have few personal inhibitions but I have chosen with care. For example, I very rarely publish any letters linking gay sex with the drug scene, other than poppers, because I have seen too much suffering in its wake. Ninety-nine per cent of my readers may be intelligent and sensible but I'm too afraid of the oddball who is turned on by the hint of danger linked with drugs to risk instilling daft ideas. I'm similarly reluctant to get too deeply involved in print when paedophilia raises its head.

I am less resistant to discussing S & M, bondage, water sports, transvestism, fisting and scat, but I guess these topics are a bit too specialised for the 'nice and homely' readers of HIM. I am very rarely approached on such topics and this is reflected in the limited references to them in this book.

And now the time has cum, as the walrus didn't say, to talk of many things — of pricks and spunk and boxer shorts, and wanker's cramp and rings...

2

WANKER'S WORLD

For most of us our first orgasm was as a result of masturbation or, perhaps, some set of circumstances which accidentally stimulated our genitals with totally unexpected results. It seems logical, therefore, to plunge straight in at the deep end and talk about wanking — the commonest and most readily available form of sexual outlet. I can't imagine that there is anyone reading this book who has never brought himself off. It is nature's natural outlet for pent-up sexual energy and thank God for it. Without it I dread to think what the statistics for rape and sexual assaults would show.

A Wanker's Bible

Dear Ray,
    Do you think it is time for a book on Masturbation — Self Pleasure for the Single Man? In an age of 'care' it would seem a good time for a real expert to collect some personal experiences and get them into print for sharing with others. Recently I counted the word 'wank' or 'wanker' used over two hundred times in a perjorative sense by about ten people. I suppose there are those who still feel it is some form of infantile or demeaning exercise.
    I know you have given practical advice about this issue in your column but, sad to say, HIM is not read by the great majority of the *Sun*-drenched public.

Darren (Bristol)

This chapter is hardly the 'Bible' Darren recommends but masturbation should be neither demeaning nor infantile. It is a very pure and noble form of sexual expression in its own right. It is most certainly not merely the poor relation of partnered sex. Skills and techniques for autoerotic arousal have been developed which can raise the one-man wank to the highest pinnacles of sexual thrill and enjoyment. Its practice is an art form and its variations are legion. It has a valuable role to play in the therapeutic relief of stress. It provides a wonderful training ground enabling a guy to explore and experiment upon himself with various techniques he may later employ with a partner. Masturbation, here's to you. Raise your glasses one and all!

Do you recall your first orgasm? I remember mine well. It was no more than two or three days after my ninth birthday. I was living in the country at the time, having been evacuated there to avoid the bombing in the early years of the war. I stumbled upon two teenage farm hands having it off in a barn. They held me face down in the hay and fucked me between my thighs. There was nothing wrong with my little willy, I can assure you. It stood up straight for all it was worth, and when they turned me over and tossed me off — to see what would happen — an incredible electric thrill engulfed my body. That was nearly fifty years ago but the memory lingers on.

Some of my readers have also written to tell me of their first times, particularly with regard to what might be described as 'Tales of the Unexpected'.

Climax Of A Sporting Career

Dear Ray,

I was about thirteen at the time, unaware of my gayness and uninitiated into the delights of orgasm. Hopeless though I was at sport I was forced to join in the qualifying swimming trials for my all-boys high school summer sports day. With the afternoon run-

ning behind schedule the teachers started holding
races with at least fifteen boys competing for swimming space across the width of the pool. I got off to a
flying start despite much frantic collision of arms and
legs. About a third of the way to the finishing line I
was shocked to discover that I was up there with the
leaders. Limbs were still bashing limbs when I suddenly felt a weird sensation in my loins and I lost all
my strength at a stroke. I was overtaken on all sides
and finished a poor last feeling hardly able to drag
myself from the pool.

At the time I thought I had pissed myself with
excitement, thinking that I had a real chance of
avoiding my usual sporting humiliation. It was some
months later that I discovered (I thought 'invented')
proper masturbation and realised that being in such
close contact with all those thrashing near-naked
boys had been the 'climax' of my sporting career.

Stan (London)

In The Pale Moonlight

Dear Ray,

My first ejaculation also occurred in a swimming
pool. I was fourteen at the time. With two or three
friends of similar age I climbed over the fence into the
public open-air pool in our local park long after
closing time on a beautifully warm summer night. We
didn't have trunks so we all went in naked and it
wasn't long before we were grappling with each
other's cocks and balls. One lad announced that he
was going to wank under the water. We stood around
watching what we perceived to be his highly novel
performance. It wasn't long before he shot and we
watched his spunk gradually mingle with the water.
We all had hard-ons but were watching, not doing
anything. Then, suddenly, I came as well, quite
spontaneously. Before that time I have no recollection

of ever having had a wank. The only stimulation had been the rough horseplay and grabbing earlier on, together with the sight of watching my pal.

That was seven years ago. I'm now a very keen swimmer. On perhaps one out of every five visits to the baths I still ejaculate quite spontaneously within a couple of minutes of entering the water and, contrary to most guys' experience, I invariably get an erection whereas everybody else shrivels up with the cold of the water.

Pete (Bournemouth)

Like Velvet

Dear Ray,

My first experience was at the age of about ten or eleven. I was struggling a bit as I heaved myself out of the deep end of the swimming pool. Then suddenly, when I was about half way out, it hit me — a sensation like having velvet coursing through the veins of my testicles. I didn't know what it was but I liked it. I don't think I even had an erection. As I only had my trunks on I think I would have noticed.

Not long after the same thing happened again whilst I was rope climbing in the school gym. It caught me about a couple of feet from the top and so paralysed me that I crashed to the floor... Pleasure followed by pain. Hmm!

Experimenting, I found that I could induce the sensation by hoisting myself up by my arms and I derived many moments of pleasure suspended from the upper bannister or the top of my wardrobe. (Is that weird, or what?) It was all great until I started to squirt an awful messy goo into my pants. That took the fun out of it. Later I discovered my right hand!

I've often wondered whether this 'happening' was the thing that shaped my sexual destiny. Had I not discovered the delights of the orgasm so early and alone, would I now be Mr Average with 2.4 kids? I wonder.

Brian (Leicester)

Strange, isn't it, how all three correspondents should have described events associated with swimming pools? There were others, of course, and one, from Mark of Crewe, was interesting. He described holding a garden hose between his legs at the age of eleven and pretending to pee for a family giggle. The vibration of the water caused him to have his first dry orgasm with parents and brother and sister looking on. It really creased him up with its suddenness. He actually realised what it was, because he'd seen his brother wanking, and was 'decidedly embarrassed'.

I don't know about Brian's surmise that had he not experienced his 'happening' he might now be Mr Average with 2.4 kids. I guess that many heterosexual males experience equally unusual first orgasms and, for the first time in this book, I use one of my regular clichés — it's just the luck of the draw!

It is said that Maori mothers used to masturbate their male babies to soothe them to sleep and certainly these early orgasmic experiences are nothing unusual. In fact, when stimulated it is quite natural for boys to get an erection and achieve orgasm, albeit dry, from quite early babyhood. Genital play is common in infant years. Four to seven year olds obviously derive great pleasure from it although they aren't aware of its sexual significance. After a relatively quiet few years, sexual experimentation usually begins again with the first signs of puberty around about age twelve, but it is often triggered earlier, consciously or unconsciously, as the above events make clear.

From time to time boys become sexually mature at quite an early age...

Early Riser

Dear Ray,

I think I must hold the record for having gone through puberty at an early age. My balls started getting bulkier and my cock started fattening out and getting longer when I was eight years old. By the time I was nine I had quite a tidy mass of pubic hair and hair under my arms as well. I can't remember when I started wanking but I know that I could shoot a really good load before I was eleven. The school doctor who examined me at that time sent me for investigations — I don't know what they expected to find — but I was OK and just labelled an 'early developer'.

I had a lot of sexual fun with older boys in secondary school and, indeed, was playing around with them before I even started there. It has never occurred to me that I should be anything other than gay. I am an absolutely dedicated, very sexually active, 100 per cent homosexual, now twenty-one years old. Do you think that my early development has anything to do with this?

Gordon (Bristol)

I wouldn't say that you hold the record for early puberty but you were certainly much earlier than most. In such cases it is usual to investigate the possibility of tumours of the adrenal glands since they sometimes cause very early masculinisation — even in toddlers. From what you tell me there were obviously no problems in your case and you haven't anything to worry about. It was just a case of the way things were!

It is always virtually impossible to be certain about the cause of any person's gayness. Your early maturation combined with a continuing strong sex drive suggests that you have plenty of male hormones circulating in your system and

I suppose that the ease with which you established sexual relationships with your fellow schoolboys, at a time when you were unlikely to have been able to do so with girls, might have been an influencing factor. However, at the end of the day, your guess is as good as mine.

Early Bearly

Dear Ray,
　　Down at the club we were chatting about our earliest sexual reminiscences.
　　I said that I remembered an uncle of mine, who was about thirty at the time, persuading me to wank him off and doing the same to me. I enjoyed the new game very much (so much for the terrible psychological trauma said to be suffered by sexually abused children) and I'm sure I remember having an orgasm every time it happened. We often used to do it because he was staying with us as a lodger over a period of about eighteen months. I've been able to work out almost exactly when it happened and I was only five or six at the time.
　　Everyone says that my memory must be playing me tricks but I'm sure I'm right. Is it possible for a boy as young as five to have an orgasm?

Reg (Birmingham)

When this letter first appeared I made no reference to Reg's comment about the lack of psychological trauma which this sexual abuse apparently had on his young mind. Several readers hauled me over the coals for not having done so. I have to make it clear that Reg's reference to child abuse was purely an aside and I didn't think it justified comment at the time. Whether or not early sexual experience has a lasting harmful effect on all young children, I believe that the risks are too great, and in some cases the effects are so serious, that there is no way that I could condone such activities. Deciding on an acceptable age of consent is a different matter, but let's not get side-tracked into that issue here.

I wonder how many of my readers started their wanking careers in the way Harry of Manchester describes in this next letter, and whether they share his current frustrations?

Blanket Bonking

Dear Ray,

When I first started wanking at puberty I did it by lying on my front and rubbing myself off against the bedclothes. I can remember the first time I did it even though I am now twenty-one. My orgasm was so mind-blowing that I had to stifle the noise I made for fear that my parents would hear in the adjoining room. I can still bring myself off with a really good sensation when I do it this way but when I turn onto my back and do it by hand the feeling isn't nearly so good. Even when I stretch my foreskin right back until my penis gets really hard and bulbous at the end I only cream the tip and don't get anything like the wild thrill I do when I rub myself off face down.

I'd like to be able to do it both ways and wonder if you have any suggestions.

Harry (Manchester)

Surprisingly enough, quite a lot of guys find it difficult to wank successfully lying on their backs and I have no idea why this should be so. However, it is fair to say that we nearly all have our preferred masturbation techniques and these are often associated with the psychological impression made by our earliest successful experiences. Harry's face down initiation to the art has left him with the conviction that this is the best way to do it.

He should persevere, though, with manual rather than the

rubbing-on-bedclothes technique because hand manipulation is much more common in partnered sex. His partner is much more likely to want to toss him off by traditional handling than to simply lie back and allow Harry to wiggle around on top of him until he cums.

Harry needs to retrain himself by rubbing on the bedclothes until he is nearly there and then turning over and finishing the job by hand. Each time he does it his hand should take over at a progressively earlier stage. And he should give himself a bit of extra stimulus when he's doing a hand job to enhance the attraction — a bit of lubrication, or perhaps with a gay video or magazine for company.

Better still, finding a regular partner to do the hand job for him may add a whole new spark of excitement into the ball game.

With the advent of AIDS masturbation has come into its own as the ultimate guarantee of safe sex. Victorian taboos have been replaced by an attitude towards positive encouragement by most medical advisers. Yet old fears die hard.

Small Cock

Dear Ray,

I started to wank at a young age (eleven) and since then have done so two or three times a day. I'm now six feet four inches tall, twenty-three years old and with a ridiculously small cock. People don't expect it when I drop my pants and that makes me feel very shy and inadequate.

Does early wanking lead to a small cock? Will mine grow any more?

'The Little 'Un' (London)

Ban The Bonk

Dear Ray,

I am what could be described as a 'fucking wanker' in that I indulge in both activities with a fair degree of regularity. And talking of degres, I've just been sitting (and passing I'm pleased to add) my BA (Hons).

Ever since I was a schoolboy I've always laid off from bonking for two or three days before a major exam. I'm not quite sure why. Maybe it's because deep down I feel a sense of guilt about it, though I don't have any strong religious convictions. On the other hand maybe it's because when I have a rest I feel less tired and mentally more alert.

This isn't really a problem letter but when I mentioned it to my kid brother, who is just as randy as I am and doing his 'A' Levels, he said he did exactly the same. Is this something within the family or is it common? Have you any comments?

Rowland (West Midlands)

Your letter struck memory chords from my own younger days. I, too, used to fight off my twice-a-day inclinations in the days leading up to examinations. I'm sure I don't know why but I guess that your analysis is as good as any. I remember, especially in school, that quite a few of my pals used to do the same. We were young and, in those days, perhaps guilt and even fear of divine retribution through being set unanswerable questions played a greater part in our abstinence than we cared to admit.

Of course, such an argument is totally illogical and I don't really think that the suggestion of a greater alertness of mind in a normally active young man holds much water either (though Olympic athletes are often discouraged from having sex the day before a major event).

•••

The above examples serve to highlight all the old wives' tales that still surround a good old wank. No, no, a thousand times no, masturbation doesn't bring you out in white spots on the palms of your hands, or drive you insane, or make you blind or stunt your growth or make you sterile or stop your cock from growing or have a hundred and one other hair-raising but cock-drooping consequences.

So, does masturbation have any associated problems? Not many. As the next letter highlights, obsessive wanking may sometimes lead to such an introverted and narcissistic attitude that partnered sex is less than satisfactory. Some of the other letters relate to real or imagined difficulties which are really secondary to the act of wanking rather than a danger inherently associated with the habit.

Wanking Woes

Dear Ray,

I've always been able to masturbate at least once every evening and in my younger days I could do it three times a day, often twice in quick succession. I'm now thirty-seven.

My problem is that when I go to bed with someone else, though I get a good erection I'm unable to cum. I don't have any problem when I'm fantasising on my own.

Terry (Bury St Edmunds)

You're quite a wanker, aren't you? Every day and up to three times a day when you were younger isn't bad going. Don't get me wrong, it's nothing exceptional. I'm still a twice-a-day guy at fifty-eight, but the key issue is the frequency of your partnered sex. You don't tell me and I really need to know.

You see, frequent masturbators who only have a partner on rare occasions run the risk of becoming so in love with themselves that having sex with someone else is only second best. They develop their powers of lone fantasy to such a high degree of sophistication that the real thing is a bit of a let down and not half so exciting. So they have no problems when they toss themselves off but when they are with a friend there is insufficient arousal to reach orgasm. This is one of the very few potentially harmful effects of masturbation.

You'll have to make a real effort to get more partnered sex and lay off the solitary DIY activity to some extent. This way you'll get the right perspective, or balance, between the two and the shared variety will become more satisfying. When it does you'll cum more easily.

In the meantime, when you are with a guy, you may have to rely on your own hand job and powers of fantasy during the final few minutes in order to bring yourself off. But encourage him to take over more and more of the action on each occasion so that, eventually, he can carry you right through to the climax.

Delicate Dicks

Dear Ray,

I've got a circumcised cock. I wank a lot on my own and make love to my boyfriend about twice a week. We are usually together for two nights running. We aren't into fucking and most of our sex is prolonged mutual masturbation and body rubbing while cuddling up close together. Occasionally we may have the odd ten minutes of sixty-nine.

Ours is a very loving and caring relationship and my boyfriend is always very gentle, but our love-play does go on for several hours and after two consecutive nights my cock is often red and sore and takes a couple of days to settle down. Both of us have average-sized pricks (about six inches) and he also wanks a lot when we aren't together. He never seems to have any trouble at all. The only difference between us is that he isn't circumcised. Is it just that my skin is more delicate, and can you offer any advice?

David (Lincoln)

Dear Ray,

I'm twenty-three years old and have, I think, a problem with my penis.

I masturbate regularly, once a night or more, and find that every so often, say once a fortnight, the area of skin beneath my foreskin becomes very red and itchy. If I continue to wank it becomes even more sore.

If I stop for two or three days the whole thing clears up, only to reappear in a few weeks when I start again.

At the moment I am without a partner. Indeed, I have never had a long term relationship. The longest was about two months. Nor am I promiscuous. I've only had five men in six years.

Stan (Bradford)

For want of a better name I'd say that both David and Stan are suffering from 'wanker's willy'.

I, too, am circumcised and these letters have brought back many happy memories of morning-after-the-night-before soreness. I say happy because, in spite of the discomfort, there is an accompanying greatly satisfying sense of relaxed fulfilment.

Those of us who are regular wankers tend to forget that the skin on our dick is quite tender and soft and can be damaged very easily. You have only to watch the attention a hard-working housewife pays to the skin of her hands to realise that the frequent wanker ought to look after his dick with similar dedication. When I'm having my morning wank in the shower I always gently massage in a few drops of skin lotion or baby oil. It adds to the fun and keeps the skin in good condition. From time to time I also massage in a little surgical spirit to harden the skin a bit. All this allows the action to be a little more robust at night.

During penetrative sexual intercourse, whether anal, oral or vaginal, the penis is slipping to and fro in a relatively well lubricated environment, but not all of us use proper lubrication during ordinary day to day masturbation. This is especially so if we are night-time wankers who set about having a pull when we are lying comfortably in bed and can't be too bothered about embarking on a well-planned, formal masturbation session. Quite often small abrasions and friction burns occur, particularly when things are a bit dry under the foreskin. Paradoxically, natural 'love juice' — which is nature's lubricant and which often oozes from our cock long before our actual orgasm and ejaculation — tends to dry very rapidly on the skin during masturbation, actually increasing the tendency towards developing small raw areas.

What's more, there are always bacteria lurking under the foreskin only too ready to get in through any break in the skin and set up an inflammation.

If you are unfortunate enough to develop a sore area it should be encouraged to clear up quite quickly with a simple anti-inflammatory cream like Savlon. Actually I'm a great believer in good old-fashioned pink Germolene (in spite of its smell). A little smeared onto a piece of lint and wrapped around the offending member works wonders.

Don't worry. You haven't any dreaded lurgy. All you have to do is treat your prick more kindly.

Subconsciously we adopt subtle different masturbation techniques depending upon whether or not we are circumcised. The uncircumcised cock is usually stimulated by pulling the foreskin to and fro over the glans with the hand gripping the shaft and moving up and down with the skin. By contrast, the circumcised cock is usually stimulated by a much more loosely encircling hand grip. The hand moves up and down over the glans and shaft producing friction because the actual skin of the penis remains fairly immobile. It's this friction which does the damage in a prolonged wanking session. The problem is one of technique rather than ultra-

26

delicate skin.

Incidentally, David's occasional cock-sucking sessions tend to make the skin a bit soggy and soft and consequently more susceptible to friction burns.

Can't Climax

Dear Ray,

My problem is that when I wank, or am being wanked, I can't climax at all. My partner can cum with hardly any effort but no matter how horny I feel sometimes I can't shoot even after trying for an hour or more. You can imagine how frustrating this can be.

Do you think that the fact that I have been taking tablets for arthritis for the past three years might have anything to do with the problem? I'm forty-three years old.

Luke (Bridlington)

I am not aware that the tablets you have been taking for your arthritis have ever been incriminated as a cause of ejaculatory failure. Nor is this a problem of masturbation as such. The most likely cause is some unrecognised guilt associated with a childhood during which sex was portrayed by your elders as dirty and prohibited. I suspect that you would have the same difficulty if you were engaging in anal, oral or vaginal penetrative sex.

It doesn't help your ego when your partner appears to cum without any difficulty, but you ought to make a great effort to overcome your inhibition because inability to ejaculate now may lead to impotence as time goes by. Persist on your own and encourage your partner to persist with you even if you do both get wanker's cramp in your wrists. Concentrate on achieving your orgasm, however long it takes, and don't take early failures too much to heart. Try a few tricks of the trade to encourage things to happen — vary your hand grip, alter the way you are lying, use a lubricant, watch a gay video. A change of routine may work wonders.

Pee Pong!

Dear Ray,

I masturbate a lot and a few days ago I noticed that my urine was starting to smell really bad. I take plenty of showers and keep myself clean. Do you think it is because I'm wanking too much?

Matthew (Newcastle)

The fear of wanking too frequently is a recurring theme.

You say quite specifically that it is your urine that smells. Maybe you have a mild infection of your urinary tract or, maybe, your urine is a bit concentrated because you haven't been drinking as much as usual. Sometimes even your diet can affect the smell of your urine — a lot of meat, for example, leads to quite a strong smell of ammonia and various amino-acids.

Whatever the reason, it has absolutely nothing to do with your wanking frequency so don't worry on that score.

So Tired

Dear Ray,

I'm perpetually tired. I don't concentrate at work and I'm very intolerant and short tempered with my family and friends. I'm totally obsessed by masturbation and do it at least twice a day. I haven't the energy, or initiative, to get myself a partner. Honestly I'm convinced that I wank too often and would like to cut it down. I'm sure I'd feel better if I did but I can't resist the temptation when the urge is upon me. I live alone and boredom doesn't help. Have you any ideas which may help me? For example I've heard that circumcision reduces the desire to wank.

Justin (Hayes, Middlesex)

Ideas to discourage wanking? Let me think .... but not too hard!!!

In the past many a poor kid has been up for the chop because his parents believed the story that circumcision discouraged masturbation. It arose when hygiene was a lot poorer than it is today and minor infections under the foreskin led to irritating sensations in the penis. This, in turn, possibly encouraged young people to wriggle and squirm and play with themselves. Circumcision may have relieved the irritation but I doubt whether it had the slightest relevance to the urge to wank.

You may not know it but Kellogg's Corn Flakes were invented in 1898 as a 'revolutionary anti-masturbation food and extinguisher of sexual desire', but I doubt whether they worked either!

You should have a medical check-up to ensure that your tiredness and irritability are not due to some other condition such as anaemia or diabetes. Loneliness and boredom can lead to apathy and I really think you should make a big effort to overcome your lack of initiative and try to mix more socially. Masturbation is a great sexual outlet on its own but you should try to balance it with some partnered activity. You are certainly missing out if you make solo wanking the be all and end all of your sex life.

The human body is very resilient and there is really no reason why those of us who are twice-a-day wankers shouldn't be able to cope perfectly well. It is said that they used to pump bromides into military recruits to dampen their ardour, but such compounds are likely to increase your tiredness so keep off them.

I'm sure the answer to your problem, if you have one, is to find a new interest or hobby and to make the effort to improve your social life.

●●●

Masturbation is a fascinating subject. There are so many ways of doing it. Sometimes, it seems, we may be at it even when we aren't conscious of it. Here's a letter which might well make quite a few readers think. How often have you come across the guy who drives you crackers because he jerks his knee up and down under the table and spills your coffee in the process?

Knee Trembler

Dear Ray,

I travel on the train to work every morning with a guy about my own age (twenty-three) and with whom I have become quite friendly though, because he gets on a few stations before me, our only social meetings are actually on the train. I've not told him that I'm gay but he knows I'm not married and all my conversation is about my male friends. Similarly he also seems to be without a girlfriend.

During the train journey I am conscious that his right leg, bent at the knee as he sits, is constantly vibrating rapidly up and down. He hardly stops at all and I'm sure he must be getting some sort of secret sexual thrill out of it. Do you think he is trying to signal to me that he is gay and should I respond?

Mark (Surrey)

Knee-trembling is a very common subconscious human activity, especially amongst men. I'm surprised you haven't come across it before. It has been said that it is autoerotic in nature, and has masturbatory significance, but, even if this is the case, I don't think you should interpret it as a sign of homosexuality. It is too common for that.

Of course, if you are becoming reasonably uninhibited in your conversation with your friend you could comment on the tremble in a way that might open the conversation to other things.

'Hey! Carry on like that and you'll jerk your leg off!' (Pause.) 'Can't you think of anything better to "jerk off" than that?'

I won't carry on the imaginary conversation any further, but such an opening remark, perhaps followed by asking why he does it and embarking on a conversational analysis of possible reasons, might well lead into interesting revelations. Once you've steered the discussion around to possible sexual motives you should be able to drop hints to which he will respond if he is on the same beam and gets the message.

●●●

I have been overwhelmed by the ingenuity adopted by habitual wankers to get their rocks off in interesting and novel ways. Some of their ideas may be more appropriately included in other chapters, but just for starters here are a few beginning with another letter from Wanker 5 whose words I've already quoted in Chapter One.

Young Scrubber

> Calling Ray Hamble,
> Unfortunately, at twenty-four I'm still a solo operator, working my own handle and crankshaft. I've found that using a body scrub (eg. with peach stone granules in it) smearing it on the glans, the shaft and under the rim of the bell-end, then wanking furiously, gets it really hot with friction. Gosh! What an explosion at the end! And it's all such good clean fun.
> Over and Out...
>
> Wanker 5 (London)

Self Service

> Dear Ray,
> I have this good way of getting my cock to shoot its load. All I do is blow up a child's swimming arm band

and jam it between the bed and the mattress with the crack showing. Then I put some KY or vaseline on my cock, stick it in the crack and fuck. Of course you've got to wash the arm band afterwards.

John (Hinckley)

Condom Be Praised

Dear Ray,

As a gay man I never thought the day would come when I would have to wear a condom for sex. When all the talk of safer sex in relation to AIDS first started the idea of putting a rubber sock on my willy quite sickened me, but now I'm totally converted. I think they're absolutely great and can't even imagine having a wank without one. By mail order they're cheaper by the gross, and that doesn't last very long.

I like the plain-ended, dry (non-lubed) type best. They fit more snugly and they don't slip off. Neither do they make your hands all sticky during masturbation. What's more, the slight reduction in sensitivity enables the action to be prolonged.

Kerry (Macclesfield)

To John I pose the question: Why have 'I' got to wash the arm band after 'he' has had all the pleasure? There is a commercially available more sophisticated form of the arm band called the 'Jac-Pac'. I seem to recall that one model can be filled with warm water, rather than air, for added effect.

I'm glad that Kerry has found the fun of a rubber even during solo masturbation. Although there is no risk of infection during DIY activity, establishing the habit of condom use at all times, so that it becomes second nature, can't be a bad idea.

Condom use during wanking affords your cock a pleasant sense of snug containment and permits you to cum without the need for a messy wipe-up. This, in turn, encourages relaxed and carefree masturbation followed by healthy uninhibited orgasm — no need to dash to the loo desperately squeezing your prick or grabbing for the tissues at the crucial moment.

Pleasing The Customer

Dear Ray,

I work in a shop on my own and my desk is just shielded by a small partition from the customer area. I have always liked tossing myself off (three to four times a day normally), but just lately I have started to wank behind my desk at work. The excitement of popping my cock back inside my trousers as a customer walks through the door is unbelievable and when I cum the climax is terrific.

I recognise this is all a bit dodgy and wonder if you have any suggestions on how I can stop it? By the way, I'm twenty- two if that makes any difference.

Robin (Brighton)

Yes, being told that you are twenty-two makes a lot of difference to readers turned on by the thought of you wanking three to four times a day and only wishing they knew the location of your shop. That's what's called 'pleasing the customer'!

What an exhibitionist you are, just like the flasher who hovers behind bushes in the park getting a thrill out of nearly being caught by passers by. I must admit I can never understand why the sight of a man's genitals in such circumstances prompts such an incensed public outcry.

I suppose that, to some extent, it depends on the kind of shop you manage. A kid's sweet store is a little different from a builders' merchant.

Musical Masturbation

Dear Ray,

You know how it is in the movies. Whatever is happening on the screen there is always a hidden orchestra providing a musical background. So we get 'murder to music', 'mystery to music', even 'mountaineering to music' on the top of Everest as if the orchestra has been shipped to the summit as an advance guard of honour to welcome the climbers coming up the hard way.

How about 'masturbation to music'? I find it quite exciting. Give me a really rousing rock 'n' roll number and I'll roll over anywhere and have my rocks off! Do you agree that 'Wanking to Wagner', 'Tossing to Tchaikovsky', 'Sucking to Strauss' or possibly 'Buggery to Bach' enhances the whole emotional achievement? What is your favourite musical turn-on?

Dudley (Witney)

'Beat out that rhythm on a drum!' Here am I with my white coat, stethoscope and all the mystique which goes with my profession at my finger tips and you come up with something like this. What a question to ask a doctor!

Well, I've read that contented cows give more milk when soft music is piped through the byre and seductive strains of supermarket musak are said to enhance the shoppers' urge to buy. So, maybe masturbation to music is the answer I've been looking for to help those with diminished libido, impotence and male frigidity.

As for myself, I seriously think you may have a point. There is a lot to be said for relaxing with one's feet up and one's trousers down, timing a toss to Ravel's Bolero. That haunting persistent rhythm which starts from nothing and takes almost exactly fifteen minutes to build up to a shuddering climax, seems just about right.

Other readers had various ideas...

Dear Ray,
Give me the cannons of the 1812 any day of the week.

Hugh (Bucks)

Dear Ray,
The Entry of the Gladiators suits me fine.

Geoff (Cleveland)

Dear Ray,
Some may consider nursery rhymes appropriate. How about, 'Rub-a-dub-dub, Three men in a tub'....

Steve (Leicester)

It was strange that nobody mentioned 'I'm a Wanker' which was in the hit parade a few years ago.

I suppose that one worry about masturbation transcends all others and it is fitting that I close this chapter with a reference to it.

Morning, Noon And Night

Dear Ray,
I am a very frequent wanker — morning, noon and night every day of the week — and there are often occasions when I make a masturbation session last as long as two or more hours before cumming. On those occasions I get quite an ache in my testicles and groin and my cock becomes very tender. You'd think such a session would drain me but within five or six hours of even the most hectic and prolonged period of action

the urge comes on me to start again. I admit that, often, I don't produce much spunk, but that's understandable. Sometimes I don't bother to ejaculate. I just have a play for about half an hour and then 'put it away till bedtime'.

How often is 'too often' and am I likely to do myself any harm?

Christopher (Brighton)

Even when occasional wanking is accepted the guilts re-emerge as the frequency builds up.

Younger readers especially are fearful that frequent masturbation may be harmful and they also worry about making it last too long or stopping short of ejaculation.

In actual fact, there are virtually no ill effects from masturbating as often as the inclination comes upon us. Our bodies are well capable of coping and indeed, if there is the need to call a halt, nature has its own in-built constraint. Once we've done it enough the urge to do it again simply goes away until we've recovered again. A prolonged session may make us feel rather tired and sometimes we can go over the top in that the urge vanishes before ejaculation has occurred and we lose our erection.

It is also said that those who develop highly skilled solo masturbation and fantasising techniques may experience a disappointing anticlimax when they actually attempt a relationship with a partner. Sometimes, too, frequent masturbators are said to be very introverted; but it is hard to say which came first, the masturbation or the introversion.

I don't think either of these issues are major problems and, if I were you, I'd take the doctor's advice and 'carry on with the mixture as before'.

3

COCKARAMA

Most of us begin to learn about our developing sexuality by exploring our own anatomy and feelings, which is why the last chapter concentrated on masturbation. It isn't long, though, before we start looking around us to see what the other guy has got.

'Mine's bigger than yours.'

'Oh no, it isn't.'

'Oh yes, it is.'

'Well, my balls are bigger than yours.'

'Yeah, but look at the length of my foreskin.'

'Yuk, who wants a foreskin? Mine's circumcised — see how neat it is.'

'But foreskins are better for wanking with.'

'And cut cocks are cleaner for sucking on.'

●●●

Man is obsessed by his cock and that of his neighbour, so in this chapter let's have a look at some of the things readers have had to say about it.

Genetics And Cock Size

Dear Ray,

I have been reading a book on genetics recently and would be interested to know what, if anything, is known about the effects of genetics on the size and structure of the penis. What can you tell me about it?

Robert (Eastbourne)

This is a topic which never goes away.

You'd be bored stiff (guess where!) if I tried to blind you with science. Suffice to say that all our body characteristics — eye colour, hair colour, bone structure, cock size and so on — are controlled by the genes which we inherit from our parents and which they, in turn, have inherited from their parents back through the generations. Occasionally a completely new body feature in the form of a mutation may occur, but these are very rare. Sometimes characteristics may remain dormant for a generation or two, or may appear only in some of the sons and daughters of a particular set of parents, so it isn't always easy to predict exactly how a baby will turn out at the time he or she is conceived. If your dad has a small cock and you've got a big one it may be because your grandfather had a big one and, who knows, perhaps your father's brother has a whopper too.

There are several distinct types of cock. In particular, there is the long dangling sort which hangs like an elephant's trunk even when it's soft and only gets stiffer, rather than bigger, when it becomes erect. Then there's the short, shrivelled kind, which seems as if it's going to disappear on a cold day but fills out and stands as proud and solid as the best of them when it's hard and yearning for action.

These variations are to do with the elasticity of the spongy connective tissue surrounding the blood spaces which become engorged during erection. When the tissue is very elastic it squeezes all the blood out of the penis in the flaccid (soft) state and so the organ shrivels very small, but when the tissue is less 'stretchy' the resting penis still retains quite a bit of blood and doesn't shrink so much. If you're a shriveller there is virtually nothing you can do to convert yourself into a dangler. Here's that cliché again — it's all the luck of the draw!

There are thin dicks and thick dicks. There are short dicks and long dicks, and those that bend upwards, or downwards, or even from side to side. Even the length of your foreskin and the size of your balls is governed by the genes on the chromosomes which come together when sperm meets egg.

The average white Caucasian male has an erect prick

somewhere between five and six inches when it's standing up to be counted. But averages are only the figures which lie between the two extremes of the range and perfectly normal erect willies have been measured at ten inches or more and three inches or less.

The same ranges occur in other races but Mr Asian Average tends to be a bit smaller than his Western counterpart and Mr African Average can usually boast a little more. The Japanese allow for this, so I'm told, when they are manufacturing condoms and some Western guys may find them a trifle tight.

Unfortunately many of my readers will not be persuaded that they have to make do with what they've got as far as the size of their cock is concerned. I get literally dozens of letters appealing for help to enhance their dick development. Some go so far as to tell me about their experiences with vacuum developers and the like...

A Right Cock-Up

Dear Ray,

I bought myself one of these cylindrical vacuum cock expanders in the hope that I could make my five-inch cock a bit bigger. I slipped the cylinder over my dick and pressed the rubber seal tightly against the pad of fat over my pubic bone. Then I squeezed the rubber bulb that sucks the air out of the cylinder and, like magic, I could see my prick swelling up to achieve an erection bigger than I'd ever seen before. I was supposed to keep it on for about twenty minutes but after about ten my cock began to get very painful so I let in the air and took the gadget off.

My cock was very swollen and pulpy with what seemed like water under the skin, especially at the base where the rubber seal had been pressing against my pubis. It took a couple of hours to return completely to normal appearance and was still uncomfortably aching after I had a wank about twelve hours later. I've been afraid to use the expander since and wonder whether you can advise me about its safety.

Jim (North Shields)

Cumming And Growing

Dear Ray,

I am twenty-one years old and for the last couple of years I have devoted much of my spare time to cock development. When I was in school the other lads always admired the size of my dick and I suppose that boosted my ego and made me cock conscious.

I started massaging it with oils and creams, always pulling and stretching it when I wanked, determined that I would concentrate on my prick just as other guys did on their bodies. About six months ago I started to use a vacuum penis enlarger regularly. I have now obtained a cylinder fifteen inches long and am making my own enlarger. Do you think that, with the aid of a vacuum pump, I'll soon be able to fill this cylinder as well without damaging any muscle tissue? Everything seems OK at the moment. I wank three or more times a day and each time I get a good throbbing hard on and shoot a good load of spunk nearly three feet when I cum.

Trevor (Penzance)

The structure of our penis is like a sponge with hundreds of tiny spaces surrounded by connective tissue (not muscle). During erection the spaces fill with blood and this state of affairs is created artificially when we suck blood into it with a vacuum pump cock expander. It is possible to develop a particularly large and hard erection by drawing in extra blood and over-stretching the connective tissue which surrounds the spaces.

Herein lies the danger. The over-stretched tissue loses its elasticity and may eventually become scarred to such an extent that it won't stretch normally at all. The natural power of erection can be all but lost. That leads to impotence. In the shorter term the weakened tissues are infiltrated with a clear fluid (serum) which seeps out from the blood and this leads to a condition known as oedema — the pulpy, soggy state and the aching described so well by Jim.

Trevor is taking quite a risk when he leaves his gadget on for several hours. Such an impediment to the natural blood flow could even result in gangrene of the penis and I'd hate one of these days for his cock to drop dead.

Vacuum expanders can be a bit of fun and a novelty aid to masturbation or lazy erections when used occasionally and for quite short periods, but they can be dangerous and the claims that the natural size of the penis can be substantially increased by their regular use are, frankly, a load of cock!

●●●

Perhaps familiarity breeds contempt because, much to my surprise, when I tried to make a selection of published HIM letters from guys grumbling about the inadequacy of their dicks I discovered that I had, in fact, committed very few of them to print. All too often those who raise the issue ask not to be included in the magazine. How I wish I had a magic growth potion — wouldn't I be just the richest man on earth! The sad saga of Lionel's idea is worth referring to...

Small Cock Club

Dear Ray,

I wrote a private letter to you recently bemoaning the fact that my cock was smaller than average and seeking ways to increase its size.

You replied that the bad news was that there was no remedy for the problem and that I would do better devoting my energy to using what I had to its greatest effect rather than becoming obsessed by my 'shortcomings'.

You added that the good news was that lots of guys genuinely preferred partners with small cocks because they felt less intimidated and threatened than they did by big ones.

Accepting all this, what do you think of the idea of forming some kind of contact group amongst the less well endowed so that we can give each other moral support and reassurance? I am sure that it would be appreciated because there are an awful lot of us who feel very inadequate.

Lionel (Hants)

I replied ...

OK, let's ask our readers, but first we'll need a volunteer to run it. I could only take on a 'first sift' of the letters.

Of course, there are disadvantages as well as advantages to your proposal. Some people are not going to be helped by belonging to a group which concentrates obsessively on the very characteristic they are trying to forget. I must admit I also wonder what you would do by way of a programme of activities to prevent the interest from flagging after the first flush of enthusiasm. After all, membership is likely to be pretty widely scattered and it isn't enough to be just an 'Under Five-Inch Dating Agency'.

●●●

My reply proved to be more than prophetic. A volunteer emerged to start the group 'For Little 'Uns and their Better-Blessed Admirers' and, in response to a number of follow-up published letters and advertisements in the HIM small ads pages, about thirty guys expressed interest. However, the initial convenor backed out, there was no replacement volunteer and, as I suspected, the group was so scattered that no programme of activities could be arranged. It was a pity and I was bitterly disappointed because I'm the sort of guy who drools over a dinky dick and, in spite of my reservations about its success, I was very hopeful that the group would get off the ground. Indeed, since I started work on this book I have been delighted to welcome such a body — 'Peanuts UK' — which can be contacted at P.U.K., PO Box 31, Aldridge, Walsall, WS9 8RH.

Fortunately not everyone is embarrassed about what they've got between their legs...

Bust, Belly And Bollocks

Dear Ray,

There's no getting away from the fact that I'm just a wee bit overweight. Well, I'm twenty-three stones actually — though I'd easily pass for just twenty-two. My tits are pretty big, which is just as well because they are very sensitive so I've plenty 'up top' to keep me amused. My belly is like a barrel which isn't surprising when I drink eight or nine pints regularly every night and I adore a chip butty — or two, or three.... But my bollocks — oh my bollocks, wherefore art thou, bollocks? They've virtually disappeared, and my dick isn't exactly what you'd consider as a potential broom handle. You could slip three of me into your average condom and the idea of wearing a jock strap is funnier than the time my grannie's knicker elastic let her down as she was leaving the church after my sister's wedding — but that's another story!

Now I've told you all about me I've forgotten exactly what I was writing to you about but, anyway, you can see I've got problems. What do you suggest?

Trevor (South Wales)

Laugh and the world laughs with you. I like your style. You don't convey the impression that your problems are getting too much on top of you. Actually, it must be a bit of a problem for anyone who tries to get on top of you — even worse for a bottom guy!

I don't know how old you are but if you have been grossly overweight and under-bollocked since infancy it could be that you have a glandular deficiency such as the one known as Frölich's Syndrome.

On the other hand, if you are merely a glutton with a beer belly, then maybe your genital ensemble has simply disappeared into the mounds of fat. It's no good me simply telling you to go on a diet when you ought to be properly investigated first and then helped with a carefully controlled programme for weight loss. I agree with you wholeheartedly that you have problems extending way beyond your inability to do much sexually lower than your bustline: for starters, think of your heart and your blood pressure.

You ask for my suggestions. Seek proper medical help from your GP and hospital consultant. I'm afraid your problem is a bit too weighty for me.

Here's one from a guy who seems to view the future with some trepidation...

Gnarled Old Oak Trees

Dear Ray,
  I'm sixty and as I get older I'm sure my cock is getting smaller. Either that or young people today are better endowed than the guys I had sex with thirty years ago.
  In those days I was never conscious of being smaller than my partners but now the young dicks look and feel so much bulkier, smoother and more succulent than my own.

Roy (Leeds)

44

That you should be so lucky cavorting around with 'the young dicks' at the age of sixty! And why not? Bully for you... Bulky, smooth and succulent. Don't whet my appetite, you naughty man!

No, there's no evidence that our pricks get smaller as we get older but, yes, there are changes with age. If we develop a middle age tummy, for example, we can easily lose up to an inch of shaft buried in the pad of pubic fat. I used to be six and a half inches but since I put on weight I've got to push the ruler in quite hard to justify a full six.

Our cocks are not exempt from the wrinkling and drying process which affects skin elsewhere on our bodies as age advances. There's a tendency to develop a sort of 'gnarled old oak tree' appearance: old oak trees don't shrink but they do look their age. And, like the thinning leaves on an old tree, we tend to lose some of our pubic hair and what's left gets greyer.

I firmly believe that most men neglect basic cock care throughout their lives. Women pay a lot more attention to the condition of their skin than we men do, and we are the ones who suffer from our neglect. A daily baby lotion massage works wonders and don't forget the maxim, 'If you don't use it, you lose it.' Regular use prevents the parts from getting rusty. You may not be as 'succulent' as you once were but there's no reason why your prick shouldn't remain both efficient and effective through to a ripe old age.

●●●

I wrote a feature article in HIM in which I claimed that, in my experience, guys with small pricks tended to be gentler, more loving and tender, and kinder than their well-blessed counterparts. It prompted this letter....

Small Cock Aggression

Dear Ray,

I was very interested in your article on cock size in HIM. I have long had a pet theory on this topic which is contrary to your observations that men with small cocks are gentler, more loving and more concerned to please as well as be pleased. I have a sneaking feeling that men with small cocks tend to feel inadequate and compensate by being more aggressive, or by engaging in certain macho activities. Unfortunately it's difficult to get the evidence to prove this.

Nevertheless, I think that a quick survey of any men who seek power, from dick-tators (sorry about the pun) downwards, would prove my case. Napoleon is the obvious example, but are there others?

On a less exalted level, I think that lager louts, football hooligans, men who tote guns (whether in clubs or in the countryside), and even weight lifters come in the same category. At least the last group presents some solid evidence!

Or perhaps this only applies to straight men? Your comments please.

Peter (Liverpool)

Who knows? You may be right. Certainly men of small stature are often said to compensate by being aggressive, forthright and proper little bastards. But maybe that's because we aren't so conscious of similar traits in bigger guys simply because we are more inclined to expect it of them.

I'm reminded of the wartime song to the tune of Colonel Bogey:

'Hitler, he only had one ball,
Goering, his balls were very small.
Himmler had something sim'lar,
But poor old Goebbels had no balls at all.'

Perhaps that proves your point.

I have no doubt that Josephine, if she were alive today, would be able to confirm or refute your supposition about Napoleon. Alas, though I'm getting on in years, I don't go back that far myself! I can only speak as I find my partners of today. I always find the less well endowed to be much more affectionate between the sheets.

Perhaps the aggro is manifest while the trousers are up but disappears when they come down and the owner is cut down to size.

●●●

Size queens abound and most of them show no reluctance to crow about their substantial endowment, though often their pride is tempered with a few points for concern.

Hard Luck Story

Dear Ray,

I'm as thin as a rake but I've got a big dangling cock which is over seven inches even when soft. My balls are quite substantial too. I'm not able to buy off the peg trousers with sufficient space in the crotch to hold comfortably all I've got on offer. I know I've given many a tailor a thrill when measuring me for slacks.

OK, so I'm boasting, but why not? There's nothing wrong in being proud of one's credentials. The only trouble is that the bulge, though real, looks artificially exaggerated and I feel that people are looking at me disapprovingly. It can be really embarrassing in straight company and I'm sure I lost a job for which I was interviewed because the woman on the panel took offence.

Bill (Scarborough)

Some people are never satisfied. Here's me thinking 'lucky old you', and there's you with a hard luck story even when flaccid!

It will be easier to treat your embarrassment than to reduce the size of your basket. Female impersonators can strap themselves down for limited periods of time in order to minimise the bulge — Danny La Rue, in his heyday, managed it beautifully in a bathing costume — but over a longer period it isn't very comfortable. Elasticated briefs don't allow for any standing room. Looser, baggier trousers may be partly the answer.

But, if you'll pardon the expression, the 'breakthrough' will come when you learn to brazen it out, overcome your self consciousness, and wink knowingly at ladies on interviewing panels!

Hark Who's Boasting

Dear Ray,

I'm in my early twenties and am an inexperienced gay male. I have been concerned for many years that men may be put off by the size of my penis — eight inches long and five inches round.

I read in a magazine once that the average penis is six inches by five. I would be grateful for your opinion.

Matt (no address given)

Now here's a challenge...

Letters like yours, without an address, stir my detective instincts. Why do you want to write in this vain manner? Do you, in fact, possess very small genitalia and is your letter an ego boosting fantasy? Are you merely keen to see your letter in print? (OK, you win!) Are you, perhaps, having difficulties in establishing meaningful sexual relationships for reason of personality or some other factor, and are you resorting to blaming the size of your penis as an excuse to explain away your lack of success?

I am sorry if I appear to have a suspicious mind but you must know that, apart from a few cranks like myself who go wobbly at the knees in adulation of five inches or less, large pricks are almost universally acclaimed. I cannot seriously think that your inexperience is due to a general turning off in response to your eight inches.

I suggest that you try to analyse your inexperience a little more deeply than you have done. There's more to you than meets the eye!

Big Boy Blues

Dear Ray,

Ever since I was in the showers at the beginning of secondary school people have noticed, and teased me about, the size of my cock which is larger than many. Most guys seem to think that it is wonderful to be large but there are problems. For example, other guys always assume that you want to be the active partner even though there are times when you would prefer to be passive. And, when you do want to be active, it is often difficult to find an arsehole that's big enough.

What happens when you wear boxer shorts? The damn thing hangs out of the bottom of them! Seriously, it is a 'big' problem in these condom conscious days. They split when being pulled on or deep inside when you're in the middle of a fuck, and they aren't long enough to reach the base of the shaft. What do we big boys do in the interests of safer sex?

Jack (Ipswich)

Son Of Big Boy Blues

Dear Ray,

As an infrequent visitor to the British Isles I only occasionally read HIM. As I am also in the medical profession I enjoy the Doctor's letters and replies.

Has anyone ever stated the disadvantages of having a king-sized cock? To be over-endowed is not always a good thing. My member is particularly gross in both length and girth and causes me a number of problems.

Firstly I can't get a really hard erection no matter how horny I feel and I usually cum when I'm only semi-hard. It might look terrific but it is virtually useless for active penetration, and, anyway, most guys can't take it without considerable pain — three cheers for masturbation! Also there is no suitable condom readily available as the ring is too tight for comfort, assuming that you've managed to get the rubber on that far.... no easy task when you're greased! And just what do you do with a huge dangling appendage when you are wearing boxer shorts; and where do you hide it in your tight swimming trunks? Letting it all hang out is not acceptable in most social circles.

For posing and photography big is great, particularly to the not so well endowed onlooker, but I really envy the guys with rock-hard compact cocks standing up proud and straight. They're much more practical and less embarrassing in the real, everyday world.

B.B. (ex-pat)

Big Boy Blues — Be Buggered!

Dear Ray,

Jack of Ipswich and ex-pat B.B. must be joking when they moan about the size of their cocks. Their apparent efforts to crave sympathy are nothing of the sort. They are both lucky men with a big basket — and they know it. Crocodile tears don't cut any ice with me. They're after maximum publicity and exhibitionist self-glorification knowing that 99 per cent of those who read their letters will be envious of their endowment. I'm just an ordinary average six inches and it hurts my ego enormously when other guys crow about their superior size.

My advice to both of them is to stop pretending that they're hard done by and to show off their armament with pride. Then the rest of us could show them proper respect and enjoy our fantasies about them.

Big Boy Blues — be buggered! Tell them to stop wingeing!

'Mr Average' (London)

Well, that's telling 'em, 'Mr Average', but I do sense a certain inconsistency in your argument when in one paragraph you say that it hurts your ego when guys crow about their size and then, in the next breath, you say that they should show off their armament with pride.

I think we have a classic case of the grass being greener on the other side of the fence. There is no doubt that penis envy causes nearly all men to wish that they were better hung than they are, but I am sure that there are disadvantages in having a 'mega-dick' and Jack and B.B. are right to point them out.

The condom problem can be partially overcome by using plain-ended Durex Gold which are designed for the 'longer laddie'. The Americans have recently made the Magnum brand available for the XXL market. Aegis, the Birmingham mail order company, sell an unlubricated Big Boy sheath. However, be warned that there are no condoms at present designed for anal intercourse and the British Kite Mark standard is explicitly for vaginal use.

Big dicks certainly do have problems entering tight holes, male or female, and they need to be well lubricated. There is always an increased risk of minor injury to the receptive partner so care and consideration is needed; the possibly greater hazard of infection entering through abrasions means that safer sex is particularly important.

The biggest prick I have ever actually measured was 11.75 inches. That was on a patient in hospital for a hernia operation some thirty-five years ago. It was quite incredible! He told me that it worked perfectly and without any problems. I can only believe that the difficulties which do arise are of a very individualistic nature, but they are none the less real for all that.

I have one regular correspondent I've never met, who swears that he is fourteen inches. I have angered him by expressing my scepticism but, as he rightly says, he is not a peep show and he won't let me visit him to see for myself unless I let him fuck me. No way! I must say, though, that even I, a small dick man, thrill to his exploits and those of his almost as large partner. They aren't exactly suitable material for this book because it very definitely seems that there is nothing whatsoever wrong with their willies!

Here's a question to which I don't know the answer....

Are The Big Boys Usually Gay?

Dear Ray,

The male pin-up mags always seem to concentrate on the most extravagantly endowed young men. It strikes me that the difference in height between say a short man at five feet eight inches and a tall man at six feet four inches is a mere eight inches, or about 10 per cent, whereas the difference between a little cock, mine at three inches , for example, and a big one at ten inches, is 300 per cent or thirty times the bodily difference. All the other appendages are generally in line; for instance, you don't find men with arms three times longer than others. What do you think accounts for the huge differences in genitalia?

Do you think that a boy's early awareness that he is perhaps hung larger than his mates encourages a penis interest which might develop into gayness? If he is aware of it others will be too, and he may be flattered by the attention and the desire of some people to get their hands and mouths around it. He is more likely to be naked in male company than female company in this formative stage — or is this just a load of old cock?

Terry (Manchester)

Let's face it, three inches and ten inches are at the two extreme ends of the usual range whereas there are a lot of men very much shorter than five feet eight inches, so I think that perhaps your 'times thirty' contrast between cock size variation and man size variation is a bit exaggerated. I do take the point of your first paragraph, however, and confess that I can't explain it. It is, I'm sure, just a quirk of nature hidden in the genes (or jeans, as the case may be!).

Your hypothesis about a tendency for the well blessed to be gay is also something to which I don't know the answer. I'm unaware of any research into the comparative cock size of gay and straight individuals. It would certainly be an interesting study, but it would have to involve a very large sample of both populations to produce significant results and I can imagine great problems in undertaking such a survey.

It might equally be postulated that boys who are conscious of being bigger than average in childhood days would be more proud to display their top-of-the-range manhood to the opposite sex when puberty arrives.

●●●

Before moving on to other topics here's a gentleman who is really expecting the research workers to investigate the finer points of anatomical detail....

Head Hunting

Dear Ray,

The knob-end of my dick, when fully aroused, is quite large and prominent at the end of my rather slim shaft. It looks a bit like a bobby's helmet.

On the other hand, my boyfriend Douglas has a shaft which is much longer and thicker than mine but his glans is quite small by comparison.

In your experience does the size of the head usually bear any relationship to the dimensions of the cock shaft? I would be interested in your comments.

Jim (Bradford)

It may be a bit of an optical illusion that a normal sized knob looks bigger on a thin shaft than it does on a thicker shaft. On the other hand, perhaps there is some genetic link between the two. Just as all faces have two eyes, a nose and a mouth yet some faces are attractive and others are ugly, so all male genitalia have a cock with a knob and two balls but some 'ensembles' are much more beautiful than others. When I admire a 'genital set' I find it rather hard to say what it is precisely that makes it desirable or not. There's a sort of balance between length and thickness, size of balls and size of cock, presence or absence of foreskin, etc., which combines to produce the finished effect, good or bad. I have no doubt that the size of the knob end has a part to play in this overall balance.

•••

Now then, wait for it, let's move on to that other wildly controversial topic — foreskins and the pros and cons of circumcision. You'd think the whole world spun around the knob ends of guys who are cut and those who are not!

What's My Foreskin For?

Dear Ray,
 What is the reason for, and purpose of, the foreskin (prepuce)? We appear to suffer so little inconvenience from circumcision and I'd like to know what benefit this bit of skin was designed to provide in the first place.

John (Roxborough)

The foreskin is a feature of all mammals and is clearly more use as a protective hood covering the glans in some species than it is in others. You should not look at its value simply in relation to its presence, or absence, in man. But, even as a man, if you were an Aborigine dashing naked through the prickly pears of the Australian Outback I'm sure you'd be quite appreciative of an all-enveloping prepuce.

On the other hand, some groups of men have been troubled by their foreskins from earliest times, mainly on grounds of hygiene. For example, the sand of desert sandstorms lodging under the foreskins of the early Bedouins caused irritation and inflammation long before the days of antibiotics. There is a beautiful wall painting in the Egyptian tomb of Ankhmahor dating back to the period 2345-2181 BC showing two youths being circumcised and, quite probably, Jewish and Muslim religious circumcisions originated in primitive medical advice promulgated by the prophets.

Fear Of Circumcision

Dear Ray,

I have had a tight foreskin for years but have always resisted circumcision fearing that the subsequent loss of sensation would diminish the pleasure of sexual activity. Eventually, after several nasty infections, I had to be done. I was very nervous but the whole procedure was remarkably simple and carried out with a minimum of discomfort.

Now, three months later, I'm absolutely delighted with the result. If anything sexual satisfaction has been enhanced and I'm kicking myself for not having had it done years ago. Please pass on the good news to anyone who is contemplating the operation

John (Sheffield)

Cut Up At Being Cut Off

Dear Ray,

I was circumcised in infancy and I'm extremely pissed off about it. I don't give a damn about decreased sensitivity, or whatever. It's just that some doctor, without asking my permission, cut off the most interesting and exciting bit of my penis. Circumcised cocks look OK when hard or semi-hard but they look pretty pathetic on the soft, don't they?

I would say to guys who are thinking about having the 'op': don't.

Is it ever really necessary to have the whole thing lopped off? Can't a tight foreskin be cured by a small incision or the removal of a couple of millimetres at the end? And don't you agree that it is an unacceptable infringement of someone's personal liberty to mutilate their body at birth?

Come on, Doc, tell us the truth.

David (West Midlands)

Circumcision Be Praised

Dear Ray,

You often publish letters from readers contemplating circumcision so I thought you might be interested in my experience.

I was thirty-five when I started to get discomfort under my over-tight foreskin. I guessed the doctor would recommend the 'Little Boy's Op' and wondered how I was going to face up to telling family, friends and workmates. However, the doc explained that I could get it done in a day — arrive at the hospital at 9 a.m. and be home in time for *Neighbours* at 5.30 p.m. It subsequently transpired that I would have to have a general anaesthetic and stay in overnight but, by then, I'd made up my mind to go ahead.

By the time I was sent for to be admitted I had my leg in plaster, having broken it in a fall. As I was off work anyway I was relieved that the problem of explaining to workmates was solved — or was it?

With screens around the bed I told the nurse all about my religion and next of kin — you'd think I was in for a heart transplant — and heard the guy arrive in the bed next to me. I wondered what he was in for. When the screens were pulled back there lay Mick who worked alongside me in the office! So much for my little secret.

Next morning, bright and early, a trainee nurse ordered us both to take a bath but I pointed out that it might make my plaster a little soggy. Sister, to the rescue, suggested an 'all over, almost' wash.

Mick and I came out of adjacent bathrooms at the same time. We were both wearing our gowns except that he had tied his up the front and mine was tied up the back. We decided that I'd put mine on correctly, so he stripped off bollock naked there and then to turn his round. I hid my final pre-circumcision erection.

Then it was pre-med time — a fistful of multi-

57

coloured pills — and I remember nothing more until it was all over.

I awoke with an excruciating pain down there, but a nurse was waiting with something to ease the agony and by the time I awoke at tea-time (no English man ever misses his tea!) all felt fine. But I realised for the first time that Mick was in for the same surgical treat. You could tell by the way he walked!

My boyfriend came visiting and asked how many stitches I had. Proudly I announced, 'Twelve'. A crestfallen Mick overheard — he had only needed ten!

Next day we were sent home and the day after that Mick was back at work. I had a couple of really rough days as my dozen stitches argued rather viciously with the top of my leg plaster, but thereafter it was all plain sailing.

I have no regrets whatsoever about having had the 'op'. My boyfriend swears that my knob is both longer and thicker: maybe he's right, but I'm not so sure. One thing is certain, though, since the 'op' I have the wildest orgasms. I'm sure that one day I'll just die! I was so active within a few weeks that the neighbours complained about the noises coming from my bedroom.

I'm no doctor, Ray, but I would recommend circumcision to anyone who has a tight foreskin. It's mind-blowing!

Ted (Sheffield)

A Cutting Experience

Dear Ray,

Some time ago I took your advice and went to a London clinic to be circumcised. Readers may be interested to learn what happened.

It was all very relaxing and civilised. I was shown into a pleasant waiting room where, after a short while, a nurse invited me into an ante-room where I was asked to remove all my clothes below the waist. The surgeon appeared and asked why I wanted the operation but was not concerned when I simply said because I felt like it. He explained that he would carry out a total circumcision and subsequently removed my foreskin to well below my penis head. That suits me, but I know I could have discussed how much I wanted removed in detail.

I entered the operating room and lay on the table. All I felt was a couple of pricks while the local anaesthetic was injected and then, after my penis was numb, I was aware of my foreskin being pulled and stretched outwards with forceps and being cut down and around with scissors. I did not feel any pain. It took about ten to fifteen minutes to remove my foreskin and a further ten minutes to stitch the resulting wound. The end of my penis was then wrapped in a bandage and I was asked to wait in the waiting room for about half an hour until the surgeon checked the dressing and was satisfied that all was well.

I was told not to get the dressing wet for three days, and then to soak it off in the bath, having added some Savlon to the bath water. When the time was up the wrappings all came off very easily but, to begin with, my penis looked a bit bruised and the stitches were very obvious. It took about two weeks for the stitches to finally dissolve away, helped by a bit of surreptitious picking on my part in the bath.

I had been given some Amoxyl antibiotic tablets to reduce the risk of infection and I took these religiously, but I didn't need the Ponstan and Valium, which I was also given to reduce the likelihood of sexual arousal and erection. For about a week I took the occasional Paracetemol when it got a little painful, but the discomfort soon disappeared.

The sensation of my first post-op erection was quite strange: not painful but strangely sexually stimulating. The shaft skin seemed to be stretched to the limit but it soon slackened off. My regular partner is delighted with the result and several people have commented on how much better my penis looks now than it did formerly. For my part I couldn't be happier though I can still just see the site of the line of stitches.

All this was in about 1989 when the cost was £190. It may have gone up a little since then. But it was certainly money very well spent.

Francis (Boscombe)

I have printed the above series of letters without comment just to show the diversity of opinion and to give some sort of insight into what it is like to go 'up for the chop'.

As for myself, I was circumcised in infancy by a butcher of a GP, who made a pretty ugly job of it. I shall never know whether it was really necessary but I can say for sure that it very rarely is. It was very popular before the Second World War as a sort of status symbol but gradually became less common with the introduction of the NHS and the realisation that most baby boys have a tight foreskin anyway which loosens up as they get older. Circumcision is still much favoured on the other side of the Atlantic.

It is very hard to answer the question whether or not circumcision enhances sexual pleasure. Those who were circumcised in infancy have no experience of sex other than as cut, and those who have the operation in adult life usually get it done because it becomes necessary due to some problem. They are usually pleased with the result simply because the problem has been relieved. Even those who get it done simply because they feel so inclined are hardly fair judges because psychologically they were tuned into the idea in the first place.

There is no doubt that a circumcision done well can be quite attractive but too many surgeons tend to forget that a pleasing cosmetic result is important. Vanity becomes important when a man's cock is on show and an untidy circumcision can be quite upsetting. Some of my friends have returned on several occasions to their surgeons to get the job done just so. Intending patients should be prepared to insist on discussing the 'end' result they prefer with the doctor before letting him loose with his scalpel.

The London Clinic referred to in the letter from Francis of Boscombe can be contacted through the S rgical Advisory Service, 108 Whitfield Street, London, W1 (tel: 071 388 1839). I have every reason to suppose that they operate to highly professional standards but, in listing their address, I cannot accept any personal liability for their service.

Tight Foreskin

Dear Ray,

I am worried about my cock because my foreskin doesn't roll over my glans when I have an erection.

My glans seems to form a larger proportion of my cock than guys I've seen in magazines. I can roll my foreskin back when I'm limp but, though I've tried, it is too painful to do it when I've got a hard-on. I have no problem in getting an erection or of cumming when I wank but I don't have the confidence to try to get a boyfriend because I don't know whether or not I'm abnormal.

I've just turned twenty-one and I'm happy with the fact that I'm gay, so I think it is about time I started to have some fun without worrying about my cock all the time.

Rick (Dundee)

Some guys have a much bigger glans than others do. That, in itself, isn't important — it's just the luck of the draw. (There I go again!) But if the 'draw' is such that you can't draw your foreskin back in the erect state it suggests that it is a bit too tight. It may well be possible to have the opening stretched under a local anaesthetic without the need for full circumcision, but you have to decide whether you really think it is worth it. After all, you can keep it clean underneath by washing when you are flaccid and the tightness doesn't seem to affect your ability to wank.

Are you sure that your hesitancy about finding a boyfriend is really because you are worried about your tight foreskin? A lot of young men who are shy and nervous about making their first sexual relationships rationalise what is, in fact, a social inadequacy by blaming some relatively minor physical imperfection. The mere fact that you wrote to me without giving me your full name and address for a personal reply suggests that you are more insecure about your gayness than your protestations about being happy with the situation imply.

With A Yard And A Half Of Foreskin Hanging....

Dear Ray,
    Some time ago, partly as a joke and partly as an experiment, I tried to enlarge my foreskin. I did this by such means as putting elastic bands around it, taping it, manipulating it and even hanging weights on it. All this worked and it now stretches about 1½ inches below the knob.
    This caused great amusement in the showers at the sports club and my partners were fascinated. I never used to draw it back even on wanking or having a pee. Now I find I can't get it back at all.
    My new partner doesn't like it. He says it's unhygienic and it's spoiling our relationship. I'm young and I'm beginning to get quite emotionally upset. I'm afraid to face an operation because of the difficulty in explaining to my parents and workmates. Is there anything I can do?

                                        Ted (Droitwich)

If you aren't too rough, and you use a little lubrication squeezed underneath, you may be able to ease your foreskin gradually back over the knob but be careful: it may get stuck and cause problems when you can't pull it forward again.

I suspect, though, that eventually you'll have to see your doctor with a view to circumcision. I don't see why, if you are over eighteen, you have to tell your parents any more than that you've got to have treatment for a problem with your penis. As far as your GP is concerned just brazen it out. Flash your dick and say, 'That's my problem. What are you going to do about it?'

DIY Circumcision

Dear Ray,

I have had a fascination with circumcision ever since I came across the word in a dictionary at the age of twelve and then saw boys in the showers who had been cut. At the age of fifteen I even stapled my foreskin back so that I would look circumcised. Shortly after I had done this I was visiting my mother who was gossiping with a neighbour. The neighbour was saying that her thirteen-year-old daughter was finding bike riding painful after female circumcision (I can't remember the circumstances). My mother then related that I had cried when I was being circumcised. Mystified, I asked her questions later on and she told me that I had been cut when I was two years old in the doctor's surgery, but that not enough had been removed. Actually I can remember at the age of three or four lying on the doctor's couch while she pulled back my foreskin.

My mother explained that I had been circumcised because in those days (1947) it was the usual thing. What's more, I was apparently a bed-wetter and since the thirties some doctors have recommended circumcision as a cure.

Adrian (Sheffield)

I qualified as a doctor in 1956 and can remember even then that some medics recommended circumcision for bed-wetting. Status symbol circumcisions were on the decline but, even so, I shudder to think of the number of 'ops' I performed on the 'Mummy's Little Darlings' of the middle classes. Thank God those days are now more or less past.

Female circumcision is performed as a ritual in certain African countries and leads to all manner of horrendous problems. I certainly don't think that readers of this book should be encouraged to follow your DIY example. That could lead to some nasty cock-ups too!

●●●

And so it goes on and on. Before finishing this chapter I would like to include just a few more letters at random to pick up on some other typical topics.

His Boomerang Won't Cum Back

Dear Ray,

I usually wank and fuck with my foreskin covering my knob — no problem in cumming at all. Recently one of my regular partners, who normally prefers guys with circumcised dicks, says he wants me to go into action with my foreskin pulled back. It turns him on to see my glistening purple bell end. That's fine by me up to a point. When I pull it back it stays back without any difficulty until I go off the horn. Then it slips forward naturally.

But I have one big difficulty. No matter how hard I try I can't make myself cum with my foreskin drawn back. Wanking, sucking, fucking are all to no avail, though there's plenty of sensation and it feels as if I'm about to shoot at any second. There's no shortage of pre-cum oozing love juice either, but that's not the same as a good old orgasm, is it? Can you tell me why and how to 'overcum' the problem?

David (London)

No, I can't tell you precisely why. You'd be surprised how fickle achieving an orgasm can be in some folk. The slightest variation from a long established routine can make all the difference and if you've been used to cumming with your foreskin forward then there is probably some minor difference in the signals transmitted by your nerve endings which simply don't register in the necessary form to cause orgasm. All the messages which prompt arousal and the thrill of foreplay are there but the final kick which precipitates ejaculation is missing.

You may have to pull your foreskin forward right at the end when you are ready to cum or, alternatively, wearing a condom may prove to be the solution because the rubber over the end may act as a false foreskin.

If you have several partners you hardly need me to tell you that you ought to be using a condom anyway.

Downbeat

Dear Ray,

Sad to say age catches up with all of us. I'm sixty-two and, though I'm still in pretty trim shape, I can't deny that 'fings ain't what they used to be'.

I was always very proud of my eight-inch prick. It used to stand up so stiff and to attention that its tip was only about an inch from my umbilicus when I stood up straight with a hard-on. But in recent years it has stuck out progressively more horizontally from my body though my abdominal muscles are still pretty taut and I'm quite slim. I haven't put on an ounce in weight in the last thirty years.

My cock is still as stiff as it ever was during erection and I've been told that it is quite normal, as older people develop a middle-aged spread, for their dick to stick out straighter. However, I haven't got a 'pot', so what's going on?

Fred (Birmingham)

You've only been told half of the reason for your situation. It is true that sagging abdominal muscles in middle-aged chubbies contribute to horizontal erections replacing youthful uprights. However, age and prolonged use also result in a stretching of the tissues which specifically support the penis. This is another contributory factor. It's one of those 'can't win' situations — even if you keep your tummy tight you still can't do much about the other.

I'm five years younger than you are and my erect dick actually points downwards rather than upwards. That's because a) I'm too fat, and b) I love to squat down and pull my prick firmly backwards between my legs from behind when I wank. Doing that regularly for well over forty years of masturbation has done a lot of stretching to my 'cord wangler'!

I don't know of any way to redress the situation though I was amused to see a kinky little 'Willy Exerciser' in a joke shop. It was like a miniature bar-weight with a hump in the bar to hang over your prick while you exercised it by trying to lift it up and down. I only mention it to point out that it is purely a fun novelty only with no chance of actual physical success.

On Pleasure 'Bent'

Dear Ray,

I have a big worry. When my dick is erect it points almost directly to the left and I find this very embarrassing. Indeed, it causes me so much anguish that I have spoken to the Samaritans about it and they gave me the courage to see my GP. Unfortunately he didn't see my dick when it was erect and simply said that I had inhibitions about it.

What can I do? I've read books which talk about surgery but I'm too embarrassed to face family and friends. I don't think I can go on much longer leading life under such stress.

Tom (Leicester)

Most pricks have a slight upward bend in them, that's normal, and there may also be a little deflection to the right or the left. This is usually quite insignificant but sometimes it can be exaggerated as a result of some developmental abnormality affecting the ligaments or tissues of one side of the penis.

Running along either side of the shaft of the penis are two bundles of spongy tissue called the corpora cavernosa (which is a bit of a mouthful even if you aren't a cock-sucker). When they fill with blood on erection they act like a pair of splints to keep the penis stiff. If one is slightly shorter than the other, or if it contains some scar tissue from some minor injury in the past, then one side of your cock swells more on erection than the other and so it develops a bend.

Quite frankly, although heroic surgery may occasionally be possible, there isn't much you can do about it, even if it is forty-five degrees or more. However, at least it's a conversation piece, you'll be surprised at the number of guys you meet who are into something 'kinky'!

●●●

That reply didn't satisfy someone who has now become quite a close platonic friend of mine.

Getting It Straight

Dear Ray,

As a doctor I scrutinise your replies to readers more critically than most yet I nearly always find myself in complete agreement with your sound common sense and well informed advice. However, on a couple of recent occasions you have perhaps been rather misleading in implying to guys whose penises are bent that little can be done and that they should learn to live with their 'conversation piece'.

You are, of course, right that minor bends are part of the normal range and are of no functional consequence and I have even seen bends of up to sixty degrees which, on an outgoing guy with a fairly flexible erection, cause no real concern. But I do see many young adults with substantial curvatures since birth and also older men who have developed Peyronie's Disease for whom even a modest curve may be physically or psychologically distressing. Bends of less than forty-five degrees can certainly be a nuisance if the erection is of the rock-solid type.

I really wanted to make the point that bent willies can be reliably straightened out by plastic surgery techniques and this can be of tremendous benefit to the patient's self confidence and morale. What's more, it is a service which is available on the good old NHS, though admittedly there are not many surgeons around who have genuine expertise in this field.

Name and location witheld for professional reasons.

How right you are. I stand corrected. Your letter went on to describe the surgical techniques involved and I should have known better than to imply so little hope to those who are 'bent' in the less disparaging connotation of the word.

Since hearing from you I have had the pleasure of meeting you and have learnt a great deal about the art of 'willy straightening'. In fact I have been most impressed to see examples of the incredible advances which have been made in the correction of penile deformities of all kinds since the days, long ago, when I was a very junior house surgeon on a genito-urinary ward.

Grin And Bare It

Dear Ray,

I've always been a naturist at heart and, though I'm gay, I would be prepared to join a mixed sex group if only I wasn't so afraid of getting an erection every time I took my clothes off. I'm sure seeing all those other guys would give me a hard-on.

Paul (Home Counties)

Sexy Sportsman Stiff In Showers

Dear Ray,

At twenty-five my sexual activity is limited to wanking three or four times a week while fantasising over gay magazine photographs.

I've recently taken up squash and, hot and sweaty after a match, I'm anxious about showering with other men. I daren't look at their bare bums and dangling cocks and balls for fear of getting a hard-on and exposing my homosexuality. Sometimes I have to rush to put my pants on while I'm still wet to conceal my stiffening cock.

> If these guys were in a shower full of naked girls they'd all be stiff as poles so it is unfair for us gay boys to have to suppress our desires and control our pricks.
>
> Jim (Haverford West)

To the above correspondents I am inclined to say, 'Here we go again'. The fear of getting erections in embarrassing circumstances is a real old chestnut. The strange thing is that, in fact, it very rarely happens. A guy is usually a bit too self-conscious to get a hard-on, for example, when he first strips off on a nudist beach. By the time he's adjusted to the relaxed and uninhibited atmosphere the problem just doesn't arise (oops! pardon the pun).

I know the warm, soapy water and the physical handling of one's 'tackle' in the showers might prove to be a stimulus, but so what? The erect penis is just as normal and just as natural as the soft organ and the most healthy advice is to ignore it totally and to hell with embarrassment. If the others want to look, well, let 'em! That applies on the beach as well, by the way. As for the presence of women, my guess is that, even in the unlikely event that the squash club boys did find themselves in a mixed shower, the probability is that the strange circumstances would stifle any erection desires unless, of course, it was all systems go for an orgy!

●●●

I never thought I'd finish a chapter in this book for gay men talking about a heterosexual orgy but that's the luck of the draw!

4

CUMMING TOGETHER

In the beginning was the wank. Then we moved on to size up the attributes of the guy next door. Now we're moving into the big league — making (and breaking) actual relationships between guys.

It is often imagined that gay relationships don't last as long as heterosexual liaisons. It is true that marriage is, in theory, a contract for life, but just look at the number which end up in divorce. Think, too, of pre-marriage days. Don't most boys and girls fall in and out of love with a whole series of affairs before deciding on that special, hoped-for, life-long partnership? I can think of many gay couples who have lived together in blissful harmony for virtually all their adult lives.

I sometimes wonder whether we don't make a bit too much of this business of short-lived gay affairs though I do suspect that gay men probably go in for one night stands and casual pick-ups rather more frequently. Maybe the lack of some kind of contractual and legally binding relationship between gay couples does encourage more freedom and opportunism but I'm not convinced at all that gay guys are very different from their straight counterparts.

Anyway, this chapter is going to look at a series of letters reflecting the kind of relationships which pervade the gay world. In earlier chapters I've been able to group several letters together and cobble a collective reply, but most of the following correspondence relates to 'one off' situations and continuity will be less evident.

In A Family Way

Dear Ray,

My father is only seventeen years older than I am and I don't know who is the randiest — him or me. Mother left us a few years ago when she found out that he was predominantly gay but, since I was gay as well and always got on well with my father, I stayed with him when the home broke up.

For legal reasons I shall draw a veil over what may, or may not, have happened between us before I was twenty-one but now that I am of age I wonder what the position is. We are very fond of each other — and why not, we are father and son — but I'm not making any admissions in print until I'm clear about the laws of incest.

Anon. (Humberside)

Even though you leave me to draw my own conclusions about your relationship with your father you go to great pains to make sure that there is no way that I can contact you personally.

With regard to any 'under age' activities which may have occurred between the two of you there is no question but that this would have been illegal. However, as I understand it, the laws with regard to incest are quite clear. They refer to sexual intercourse between men and women who are related in various ways. There is no mention of such relationships between men and other men. Quite apart from this, the question of what constitutes sexual intercourse has not, to my knowledge, ever been completely defined in the homosexual sense.

I am not a lawyer and hesitate to offer legal advice so I shall take a leaf out of your own book and leave you to decide whether or not you and your father are in the position of being consenting adults in private within the meaning of the law. Don't forget, though, that simply because you are now twenty-one all that may have happened before is not forgotten. The long arm of the law can still catch up with you.

A Bit Complicated

Dear Ray,

I'm now fifty-six and 100 per cent gay, but in my younger days I liked it both ways. In fact I had to get married at the age of twenty just in time to legitimise the daughter born to the girl I was going out with. Because I had so many boyfriends my wife couldn't stand it and we were divorced five years later but we remained good friends and we had it off together from time to time.

One night I went to see my ex-wife but she was out and I ended up in bed with my daughter, then fourteen, instead. To cut a sad story short she became pregnant and had a son and I did time as Her Majesty's guest for incest.

My son, by my daughter, is now twenty-one and he's gay. What's more, in spite of the age gap, we're in love and having it off together regularly — in private and by mutual consent, of course.

Where do we stand in the eyes of the law?

Anon. (London)

Well you may ask! I think, once again, that the simple answer is that since your son is of legal age to consent you are not committing an offence provided that what goes on between the two of you is strictly in private. I hope, though, that you won't quote me on that. Go and see someone in the legal profession.

But why do you want to tell me all this? Surely the fewer

folk who know about your complicated life the better — or are you just trying to shock me?

Foiled again!

Time Marches On

Dear Ray,

My lover and I have been together in a fairy-tale relationship for twenty-five years. He's a gem of a guy who picked me up when I was a bum-boy on the game at Piccadilly Circus in 1962 and he's given me a wonderful home and happiness which would never have come my way had he not arrived on the scene. I love him very dearly but a problem is developing and I need your advice.

He is twenty years older than I am. I'm now forty-five and he's sixty-five. When we first met the age gap didn't matter and there were so many stars in my eyes that I never thought of the future. Now I still have a very lively libido and want to continue a full and varied sex life while he admits that his energy is flagging. He cannot keep the same strong erections that he used to, he's content nowadays with sex just once or twice a week and even then it's a very leisurely and laid-back event.

I don't question that his love for me is as deep and loyal as it ever was, and I sympathise with his changing pattern, but I'm beginning to seek relief elsewhere behind his back. I feel a real 'shit' about it, but when the urge is upon me I can't resist the temptation. I've suddenly realised that I'm dependent upon his charity, for the present, and his will, for the future, for everything I have in life. It seems my heart is in the right place, but my prick is in the wrong one.

Chris (Nottingham)

For readers with calculators let me begin by explaining that your letter was first printed in the summer of 1987.

You are not the first to face this kind of dilemma and you won't be the last. You are obviously a sensible and caring individual but any advice in which I appeal to you to exercise restraint, and which emotionally plays on the need for you to be loyal to your lover, is probably going to be a non-starter. The trouble is that when the urge is upon you the werewolf within you takes over and all your high-flying ideals go out of the window.

You have either to construct a mighty web of deceit and lies to hide your clandestine activities, in the hope that you won't be found out, or you have to choose your moment to talk the whole problem through with your lover, hoping that he will be able to come to some compromise which allows you some freedom. After twenty-five years I would hope that you know each other well enough to take the latter course of action.

Not Too Old At Fifty-Four

Dear Ray,

I'm fifty-four. For about ten years I looked after my aged mother until she died about a year ago; so I wanked regularly and led a fantasy life.

Recently I've had an obsession to pull a guy half my age. I'm slim, six feet, 40-34-39, with thinning hair. What do you think my chances are? It wouldn't be just for fun. I'd like to build it into a long-lasting relationship. Four weeks ago I stopped tossing off and now I'm getting erections everywhere and then I just have a wet cock.

Do you think I should keep on trying to make contact?

Peter (Swansea)

Of course you are not too old at fifty-four. I'm fifty-eight and I can assure you that there's plenty of life in this old dog yet. You can be certain that there are plenty of younger men who would welcome a meaningful relationship with someone of your age.

The only word of warning I'd like to sound is against allowing yourself to be hurt in, say, ten to fifteen years' time. At fifty-four you can easily be attractive to a twenty- seven year old but you may be less exciting when you are, say, sixty-five or seventy. Your partner will still only be in his early forties. Perhaps he'll feel like 'shopping around' and leave you high and dry just when you reach the time in life when you need his support.

Why have you stopped tossing yourself off? Enjoy it while you're young!

Youthful Pleading

Dear Ray,

I'm a sixteen year old who is gay. My mum and dad don't know and I could never tell them because I would feel a let down to the family. I just feel so depressed and pissed off. I don't have much of a social life and I just want to meet some other gay people in my own area and of my own age for a good time and a laugh. I can't wait until I'm twenty-one — it's too long! Even when I'm at work I can't stop thinking about men. It makes me feel so down. What can I do?

Richard (Brighton)

Yours was the letter I pulled from the hat. I get literally dozens of pleas from young guys between sixteen and nine-teen scattered all over the country expressing sentiments similar to your own.

Some sixteen year olds who believe themselves to be gay go on to develop heterosexual interests so it is unwise to come out too soon and find yourself labelled gay with all the aggravating social consequences that may entail. The trouble is that a gay label, even though it may only be a passing phase, tends to encourage some young people to believe that there is no turning away from homosexuality. So they just follow the gay track through life and resist any inclination to explore other avenues of sexual interest.

However, most mature youngsters know exactly what they are from an early age and don't change their sexual direction. All the letters I've received are very articulate and convincing but the law as it stands makes it impossible for me to say anything which might be construed as encouraging homosexual acts under the age of consent, which is currently twenty-one.

In 1979 a working party set up by the Home Secretary to consider the age of consent recommended that it should be lowered to eighteen but the Government never acted upon it. So there remain many thousands of young people desperately lonely and frustrated like yourself — just waiting to become within the law. In the meantime, in some parts of the country groups have been set up for young people and you should be able to find out about them from local Gay Switchboards, Helplines, etc., or from the small ad columns of *Gay Times*. Penfriend agencies can also be contacted in this way.

About the only word of encouragement I can offer is to say that sometimes the most incredible things happen. Just read the letter a little bit further on under the heading 'A Breath Of Fresh Air' for example.

Lonely Hearts Club

Dear Ray,

I'm twenty-three, gay, five feet nine inches, and slightly overweight. I'm also unhappy, lonely, depressed and unwanted. Not many people know I'm gay and I'm too shy to go alone into gay pubs, clubs, etc. How do I go about meeting someone who is shy like me and who wants primarily a loving relationship with sex that develops from such a friendship, rather than sex for its own sake?

If I were to go cottaging in the local gay toilets I think I'd be too shy to make the first move. How do I attract someone to me?

Tony (Leeds)

First of all stop worrying about being slightly overweight. It takes all kinds to make a world and there are lots of guys who go for the 'fuller figure'. I'm not surprised that you feel unwanted if you are too shy to make your gayness known to people who would be attracted to all your better features. You are young, your diffidence means that you are not a 'screaming queen' likely to prove an embarrassment to other gays who are equally restrained in their overt gay behaviour, and you want, first and foremost, a loving relationship. These are all attributes which make you 'a very saleable product'.

I get many letters from sad and lonely gays like yourself but I'm afraid I can't act as a lonely hearts contact agency. There are many dating agencies advertising regularly in the gay media. They are far more efficient in finding suitable mates than I would ever be.

I always advise correspondents to place their own contact adverts rather than replying to those of other people, because, through your own box number, you can preserve your own anonymity while you sort out the replies and get in touch only with those who interest you.

If you are too shy to go into a club I can't see you as being a very successful cottage cruiser but, if you do try it, I strongly advise letting the other guy make the first move. There's nothing more upsetting than discovering that you've been trying to touch up a plainclothes 'dick'. Be patient, everything cums to he who waits.

●●●

The above reply of mine stimulated a barrage of correspondence.

A Saleable Product

Dear Ray,
How on earth can you describe shyness as a 'very saleable product'? Only in the last year or so have I had enough courage to stick my head out of the closet (in more ways than one), and it was bloody difficult. Most people have little, if any, sympathy for shy guys. Fair enough: that I can accept and live with — there are worse things in life than being gay and shy — but don't make shyness out to be something that it is not.
Before I give the impression that I take my shyness too seriously, is there anyone out there who thinks that it really is 'a very saleable product'? I'll be more than happy to sell it to them. You are right in one sense though. I'm certainly not, and never will be, 'a screaming queen'.

Jim (West Midlands)

I still defend my point of view. The quiet, demure, unassuming, socially withdrawn individual — though not everybody's idea of a bundle of fun — is very attractive to a lot of people. His very reserve is appreciated, especially by those who are themselves rather insecure and alarmed at the prospect of being dominated. Shy people tend to be a good bet as far as discretion and sincerity are concerned.
Anyway, I do think that your letter is rather callous. I'm doing my best to give shy people a new faith in their own personality — an ego boost to help their confidence — and there you are pulling the rug from under my feet!

Let's ask the verdict of readers. If I'm wrong, I'm man enough to admit it.

Jim Again

Dear Ray,

I was offended by your reply to my earlier letter complaining about your description of shyness as a 'saleable product'. I had no intention of pulling the rug from under anyone's feet, or, indeed, of undermining their confidence. I merely wished to convey shyness from the other side of the fence — which is not exactly a green pasture.

If what you say is true then maybe we silent types have something in our favour after all.

Jim (West Midlands)

A Supporting Word

Dear Ray,

Thank you for your personal correspondence and your printed comments on that 'saleable product'. You will probably be surprised to know that I more or less agree with everything you have said. In all my adverts I have been using the phrase 'shy, quiet persons welcome' which, I suppose, just reinforces your argument. One has to try to think positive. Indeed, last year when I went to group therapy for my depression I upset the group by telling them that there was too much negative thinking. It is most important to try to see the bright side of things.

Peter (Huddersfield)

To Jim and Peter and dozens of others I express my thanks for all the letters I received. Some were supportive, others quite vitriolic in their condemnation. I have high hopes that my supporters will have acquired a new insight into their problem which will go a long way towards overcoming it. I kneel chastened before those who have convinced me that, for them, their shyness is irredeemable. I am saddened for them as they wallow in their quagmire of self-pity. In trying to project the endearing qualities of shyness I did so with the kindest and most positive of intentions. I have to acknowledge that there are those who are unable to accept my line of thought.

I don't use the phrase 'quagmire of self-pity' in any intentionally derogatory sense. This is a standpoint from which I see no easy way to escape, but there is a subtle difference between genuine shyness and using it as an excuse to conceal a massive inferiority complex. If a person cannot turn his shyness into a saleable advantage, then he either accepts the challenge to overcome it by his own prime endeavour or he goes down beyond redemption.

'D' For Danger

Dear Ray,

My wife recently found a loving letter from my married male affair signed simply with his initial 'D'. She has assumed that 'D' is a woman and knows nothing of my predominantly homosexual nature. She is very anti-gay in all her thinking, especially since the AIDS epidemic, so I've just remained dumb over the years or taken the easy way out and agreed with her sentiments.

Now she believes that by talking through the problem face to face with 'D' she can 'sort her out' and save our marriage. She insists that I arrange a meeting. Perhaps I'm silly, but I would like to stay with my wife for the sake of our children and because I'm still fond of her. 'D', similarly, is anxious to preserve his marriage. Where do we go from here?

Sam (Harrogate)

Obviously, if you want to preserve your gay secret, a meeting between 'D' and your wife is a non-starter. I doubt whether coming out to your wife at this stage is likely to be helpful either.

I can only suggest a 'dastardly plot' between yourself and 'D' whereby you send him a letter, ensuring that the wording is seen and approved by your wife, saying that now your affair has come to light you realise that your priorities lie at home and that you wish to stop seeing 'her'. 'D' will then have to reply acknowledging your point of view and promising not to see you again. Your wife can't force 'D' to appear before her and you'll just have to be a damn sight more careful about communicating with him in the future. Why not invest in a convenient PO Box where you can collect your mail?

I never like the idea of living a lie but, if you are prepared to accept the situation in order to protect family integrity, I think you should play down the whole business. Tell your wife that 'D' went over the top in 'her' infatuation for you and that it was never fully reciprocated. I cannot see any point in increasing her anguish by bringing up the question of your gayness.

Dangerous Situation

Dear Ray,

I'm in the fifth form at school and having a relationship with one of my teachers who is twenty-eight. It started about a year ago when we were alone together in the gym and he wanked me off. He said he was turned on by me because I was quite hairy for my age. Although I was a virgin up to that time I really fancied him. After that first time we often had sex together and shortly after the summer holidays last year we were nearly caught together in a storeroom by the headmaster.

One Saturday at Christmas time he invited me

back to his flat and for the first time we went all the way. It was fantastic. He knew it was my first time so he was very gentle with me. Now I go every week to his flat to make love. He says he is madly in love with me and I'm totally in love with him too. But I'm scared about what would happen if we were discovered. He might go to jail and I might be expelled.

Now a very attractive boy in my own class keeps making passes at me, especially in the changing rooms. I fancy having sex with him for fun, not love, but I'm afraid that my teacher friend, who can see what is going on, will get jealous. I don't know what to do. I just seem to think sex all the time and it is affecting my school work. I do feel that I should stop it with my teacher and stick to someone my own age, but I love him so much and he has asked me to move in with him when I leave school.

Anon.

It is just as well that you wrote anonymously and I couldn't even decipher the post mark. I hope you can recognise your original very long, highly erotic and explicit letter in its abridged form. It made very exciting reading and I began to wonder whether you were composing a fantasy of what you would like to happen or whether you were completely genuine. Boys of your age often develop intense crushes on handsome teachers, especially those who are well hung and with whom they may share a shower after a sports session. Don't think I'm just dismissing you as a 'romancer' but I have to make the point to warn other readers not to be taken in by everything they hear.

If you are completely genuine I do hope that you realise what a dangerous situation your teacher friend could find himself in if you so much a breathe a word about what is going on to an indiscreet source. That he 'might go to jail' is the understatement of the year.

I cannot publicly condone your relationship which is totally illegal — unless you are a twenty-one year old fifth former! For both your sakes, ease out of the situation now. A sexual relationship with a boyfriend of your own age would still be illegal, in theory, but the consequences of being found out in those circumstances are likely to be far less disastrous.

Adolescent Crush

Dear Ray,

Can a person be gay without knowing it? I am in my fifties, and very definitely gay, but I have withheld this information from a young friend with whom I have a close and entirely platonic friendship. He is only nineteen and, more to the point, I am particularly friendly with his parents and I certainly don't want to rock the boat by sailing too close to the wind with him.

Recently I told him that I was going away for a few days with another young friend of mine (twenty-two) but, of course, I didn't let on that this guy is my 'toy boy' with whom I have a very steamy sexual relationship.

Although my nineteen year-old friend knows my 'toy boy' I have no reason to suspect that he is aware of anything special or different about our relationship. Nevertheless he has become intensely jealous and wildly possessive of me. Indeed, he is mounting an almost obsessional crusade to prevent me from going away with my sexual affair. I know my platonic friend to be very naive about sexual matters and I'm completely taken aback by his sudden, cloying affection for me. I am unnerved and don't quite know how to cope.

Malcolm (Bournemouth)

Teenage crushes on older men are very common, as I explained in my answer to the earlier letter from the schoolboy who was having an affair with his teacher. Unfortunately, vulnerable professionals, eg. church and youth leaders, social workers, teachers etc., are often tempted to respond by making sexual advances which lead to complaints, courts, convictions and chaos!

Sometimes these adolescent crushes are genuinely homosexually motivated, either with or without the full understanding of the young person concerned. In these situations, when the older man goes along with it and allows, even encourages, things to happen, a good time is had by all. Sometimes though, even if there is a sexual motive for the crush, it is so heavily sublimated that it never surfaces. It is in these cases that all hell is let loose when the older guy makes a move.

Who can tell what your young platonic friend is thinking? Clearly he is very emotionally put out at the thought of your affections being transferred elsewhere. However you would be placing yourself at great risk if you were to believe that his behaviour constitutes an invitation to have sex. Don't forget that you, yourself, may be feeling a little bit guilty about going off with your twenty-two year old and could be reading a little more into the other lad's behaviour than is actually the case.

A Breath Of Fresh Air

Dear Ray,
    Here's a story with a happy ending for a change as a counterbalance to all the guys who fill your columns with problems.
    Twelve years ago, at a school camp, I was seduced by a thirteen-year-old lad. I was seventeen at the time but very innocent: maybe I had a wank about once a month. In the tent one night the youngster started asking me about sex and insisted on showing

me his first few wisps of pubic hair. I really wasn't interested and told him to put it away. Then he asked if I had a girl friend and I replied that I just wasn't interested in sex at all. However, he persisted and asked me how often I wanked. He told me that he had started doing it about a year before with a boy of his own age. Eventually he persuaded me to show him my cock and when he took hold of it I became aroused and that's how it all started.

Disaster overtook us, however, in that we were caught in the act by a teacher who was suspicious of the noises we were making. There was a hell of a rumpus. No one would believe that it was the youngster who had started it all and I was sent home in disgrace. The remaining year of my school life was made virtually intolerable.

But there was one saving grace. The young lad stood by me. He was so kind and supporting that we soon fell in love, making sure that we were never caught again. I'm now twenty-nine and he's twenty-five and, with the approval of both sets of parents, we've just bought our first house together. I just can't put into words the purity and depth of our love for each other. From an extremely dodgy beginning has emerged something very wonderful which straight society would clearly have wished to destroy at its genesis. Isn't life simply marvellous?

Cliff (Winchester)

For once I don't have to come up with some 'instant coffee' antidote to someone's gay problem. It does us all good to be able to share in the happiness of a life story which seems to be turning out so well after a shaky start. There is no doubt that your story highlights the need for society as a whole to discard prejudice and allow young people to develop their sexuality in their own way.

The other thing about your letter, of course, is to remind us that for every gay who writes to me with a problem there are probably hundreds of others who are happily in tune with their homosexuality and who will never feel the need to write to a column like mine.

The First Move

Dear Ray,

I'm a gay, twenty-three-year-old, six feet three inches bodybuilder. The problem is that I have fallen in love with a fellow bodybuilder who is not gay and is only twenty-one.

He knows I'm gay and he believes that gay people shouldn't be hassled, but he is very careful what he says to me and he won't get undressed or shower in front of me. I've noticed, though, that he's always keen enough to look me up and down when I'm naked and to pass complimentary comments about my body.

He wears really tight jeans which show off a nice tight arse and crotch and he sometimes puts on a pair of cycling shorts which show a fantastic cock silhouette snaking down his thigh.

What I want to know is whether I should make the first move and how I should go about it. We are close friends, but not that close. It's just that he has a fantastic body but won't let me touch it and I get so madly horny.

Kim (Warwick)

Watch it! You are describing a typical straight 'prick teaser'. You aren't in love with him, just his body — and in particular the parts he won't show you just to tantalise you.

You make a first move at your peril with guys like that. You obviously enjoy your work-outs in the gym. People may know that you are gay and happily accept the situation provided that your behaviour is acceptable but you could be out on your arse if you started making advances. Then you would lose your friend and your hobby.

If I were you I would just go on developing the social side of your friendship over a coffee or a pie and a pint in a local pub. Eventually you may be able to bring the conversation around to sexual matters. It certainly isn't for me to teach you how to seduce somebody, but remember: 'Softly, softly, catchee monkey.'

Driven Apart By A Fart

Dear Ray,

I feel silly even talking about my embarrassing problem but it is beginning to affect my sex life.

My present boyfriend is my first 'regular' and we've been going out together for about four months. At first I was afraid to let him fuck me but, about a month ago when I was sufficiently drunk, I gave in and let him do it (with a condom of course). It was probably the most enjoyable experience I've ever had and we've done it several times since.

Unfortunately, for some unknown reason, for a couple of days after we've fucked I seem to fart uncontrollably — don't laugh, it isn't funny! I thought it was probably just because it was the first time and that it would resolve itself once the muscles got used to it, but it's not and, as a result, I don't want to be fucked any more. I just can't stand the embarrassment of trying to stifle several farts every hour, but my boyfriend doesn't seem to understand because, in the beginning, I enjoyed being fucked so much. I'm terrified of losing my boyfriend. What can I do?

Ian (Ayr)

I agree it would be a tragedy if a fart were to prove a blow to your love life.

The key to successful anal intercourse is to be able to relax fully the sphincter muscle at the entrance to your arse. You've obviously mastered that more easily than you anticipated at first, but now you have to learn how to tighten it up between times. Once your muscles have been stretched by a good fucking you have to consciously exercise them to tighten them up.

Some folk find it helpful to lie on their back with their feet up on a low stool or coffee table and insert a finger or a thin object like a well lubricated pencil (don't leave go!) and then practice tightening the muscle around it for several minutes two or three times each day. Actually, 'shrugging' those muscles every few minutes can be done as you go about your daily life without any onlooker being aware of what you are doing. In time, and with training, you should be able to overcome this common aromatic problem.

On Morals And Principles

Dear Ray,

My lover is very kind and considerate. Although he knows I don't like it he very often sleeps around with other guys he has picked up in cottages and saunas. He is quite prepared to admit it but claims that when the opportunity presents itself he can't resist the temptation. He says that he always has a very high regard for the need for safer sex and I believe him because he has always insisted that he isn't into anal sex anyway and he will never fuck me or let me fuck him, even though he knows that I would like both these things to happen.

But it isn't the safer sex aspect that I'm really concerned about. I'm a Christian and I believe that the sex act is very wonderful and symbolic of the love between two people. Even though he is honest with me and tells me when he has been with another man it hurts me deeply because it goes against what I believe to be moral. I, too, am tempted from time to time when I meet attractive guys who are more than willing to drop their trousers and bend over. It would certainly relieve my frustration at my lover's refusal to let me get inside him. But I resist such temptations on principle. I think I'm right and my lover should consider my feelings a bit more. Don't you?

Lenny (York)

The age-old conflict between 'lust' and 'love' is not one which can be easily resolved. Your Christian beliefs give you the strength to resist temptations which you face and you are quite right to conduct yourself accordingly. You would feel guilty and ashamed if you were to do otherwise, and that wouldn't be healthy.

However, you are not your lover's keeper. Clearly he cannot accept your moral philosophy and his sexual behaviour seems to be governed by physical urges which are stronger than your own. He is honest with you and, as you say, he is kind and considerate when he is with you. I think you have to accept that his love for you is as genuine as yours is for him. Don't try to force him into a pattern of behaviour which would put him under great emotional and physical distress. That wouldn't be healthy either.

No Prizes For Guessing

Dear Ray,

After spending ten years with the same partner I'm finding him boring. We live over five hundred miles apart and I keep thinking before I visit him, or he visits me, whether I want to see someone who is overweight, bites his finger nails, picks his nose, is developing ugly varicose veins, doesn't wash often enough, has false teeth, is older than I am and only talks about his work. On my way to spend a weekend with him I feel happier, but as soon as I've been at his place for a couple of hours I feel I want to get away. I start to find fault with things and before we even get into bed together we start quarrelling.

I have recently joined an outdoor gay club near my home and I enjoy being with the members more than with my lover. They make me feel happy and, though I didn't join the club for sex, I have been to stay with some of the other guys and have had some really good times. I've started to do exercises to get a better body but my partner isn't the least bit interested in anything I do. He tells me that he doesn't like my new friends and doesn't want anything to do with them.

Why is he so boring?

Finlay (Inverness)

Your partner sounds a real groovy turn-on! To be sure, I can't for the life of me think why you don't leap onto the train every Friday evening imbued with a sense of longing, passion and irresistible desire. The pounding in your heart and the throbbing in your crotch must drive you to distraction as the night train hurtles you to the joyous weekly reunion which awaits you at the other end. On those sad weekends when you can't get away and are forced to stroll in the open air amongst the heather and with congenial company; when the birds fly overhead; when a great day out is followed by a dreamy night with affectionate new, gay friends... Think of what you're missing: those fabulous varicose veins, those wonderful false teeth and that beer belly... Then you can ask yourself again, 'Why is he so boring?'

Innocent Fears

Dear Ray,

I'm frightened and I need your advice.

I'm twenty-two and was recently fined for cottaging. It was a 'fair cop'. I was actually caught with the local vicar having a blow job! I'm not complaining about that. It caused a lot of family upset, though, and my parents are still very suspicious every time I go out in the evening. I know I could tell them to mind their own business but they stood by me and I love them for the understanding they showed. I don't go cottaging anymore, but I still have an active sex life.

The trouble is that, at home, I have no option but to share my bedroom with my seventeen-year-old brother who is a mentally handicapped Down's Syndrome boy. He has recently taken to wanking and being very indiscreet about it. He has told me things which lead me to believe that one of the staff at the day centre which he attends is having sex with him but I have no proof and it would only be my brother's unreliable word against that of a respected centre worker.

I'm terrified that when my brother is caught, as I'm sure he will be — because he's quite capable of pulling his prick out on the school bus and starting to have a wank — my family will blame me for having abused him at night. My conviction will lend credence to such an accusation though it will be completely false and I will have great difficulty in proving my innocence.

J.B. (West Country)

You clearly see yourself as being between the Devil and the Deep Blue Sea. If you voice your concern to anyone your word is suspect because of your recent conviction. On the other hand if you say nothing and your brother is caught openly displaying homosexual tendencies the finger of suspicion will point at you.

Faced with these two alternatives I think I would be inclined to pluck up courage and come clean about what you suspect is going on to your parents. If they stood by you at the time of your court case it means that they ˙espect you and I suspect that they will accept your word. If, however, you stay silent and in due course people turn on you and expect you to demonstrate your innocence it will not help if you are forced then to say that you've had your own suspicions for some time. People will only say that you should have said something earlier.

'Yukky Sucky'

Dear Ray,

Although ours is not exactly a master/slave relationship, I do like my boyfriend to force me into submission and I enjoy a really good caning before he administers an enema and then fucks me. I'm not very brave and I cry like a baby from the pain but it relaxes my arse so that he can stick tubes and pricks and things in much more easily.

Because of the bowel washout I know my inside is clean before he screws me but he always pulls out before cumming and then expects me to take him in my mouth to finish him off. I just can't get away from the idea that that's 'yukky' and I really don't like it. But if I don't agree he thrashes me again and, by now, my bum cheeks are usually too sore to take any further punishment. So, I'm afraid to refuse but I loathe having to agree.

We really do get on very well together and before we start having a sex session I'm so aroused that I

seem to forget that I'm going to have to make the
same distasteful decision yet again.

Tony (Stoke on Trent)

Very many active gay guys quite happily take this kind of
thing in their stride and will wonder what you are making all
the fuss about, but I imagine that there will be many others
who will be quite revolted at what your lover expects of you.
It's all a matter of taste! A lot of people will be sympathetic
towards your dilemma.

Most of us know that 'love is blind' so that when the heat
of arousal is on we fail to see the consequences of what we are
about to do even though we have trodden the same path many
times before.

You may find it easier if you can persuade your boyfriend
to wear a condom while he fucks you (he should be doing so
anyway), and to remove it before he gets you to suck him off.
Alternatively you may be able to pause in your passion long
enough to wipe him clean with a warm, damp flannel (make
it a sexy interlude). If neither of these solutions is acceptable
then I'm afraid you'll have to learn to say 'No' very firmly, and
be equally adamant about not accepting the repeat chastise-
ment.

Getting A Bit Rough

Dear Ray,

My partner and I have been together for a few
years now and we've had a master/slave relationship
just for fun, but recently things have been getting a
bit rough. He's all muscle and about three stone
heavier than I am so that when he pins me down I
can't move. Then he beats the shit out of me until I
can't feel a thing anyway and fucks me while I'm still
half-dazed. I love him very much but it's scary. He

loses his temper very easily and seems to like me to be completely subordinate to him even though he is quite the opposite and over-protective towards me when we are out together.

I've confronted him about it and shown him the bruises to prove it, but I must be going soft because, even though I work out regularly, I can't keep up with him. Sometimes I'd like to kick his arse, but I don't because I'd like to reach my twenty-fifth birthday!

He has some toys in a chest in the basement. I used to like strapping up for him but now I get nervous. The other night I was awakened by pain and realised he had strapped me down in my sleep. He's very demanding and insists on having sex whenever he wants it — even when I'm not in the mood.

How do I deal with this situation without losing him? I am a bit of an introvert and rather naïve. I have no-one else to turn to and guess I need some new friends. I need some help. I don't want to drown, just some calm sea.

John (Lancaster)

Big oaks from little acorns grow! S & M activity can be addictive. What starts as fun can escalate out of control as partners become more involved in their search for the holy grail of the 'mega-orgasm'. You must make a stand now even though you may fear for the future of your relationship. You may even have to gamble on leaving him for a while. When he asks you to go back to him you make it clear that you return only on your terms. If he doesn't ask you to go back to him then you know that he was only using you for his own satisfaction and so wasn't worth knowing anyway.

I agree with you: you must make the effort to find some new friends.

Missing His Master

Dear Ray,

Over a three year period I became progressively more addicted to my boyfriend's sadistic tendencies. What started with mild spanking during love making moved on to my being tied to the bed and thrashed with a belt before my lover fucked me. When I became his total slave, doing all the household chores and serving his every need under threat of punishment, I decided enough was enough and left him.

I now have a new boyfriend and find that I still want him to beat me and treat me rough, but he says he loves me too much ever to hurt me and thinks I'm perverted.

I have become wildly jealous of my former lover's new boyfriend who he beats regularly and treats as a slave. I've asked to be taken back, even as 'second fiddle', providing I can serve him and receive the strap as a prelude to any sexual acts he might want. He has refused even though I have degraded myself by begging him in front of his new lover and offering to act as slave to both of them.

I know this is not normal and want to be cured of my obsession, but even thinking about my past life under his control makes me painfully horny.

My new lover says he will stand by me and help me through any treatment I may need. Where can I turn for help?

John (Northampton)

Once you are tuned into the 'heavy' sexual scene it isn't easy to revert to the 'lighter touch' and still obtain total orgasmic satisfaction. Your former boyfriend recognises this and is simply exerting his sadistic nature in refusing to take you back. He is enjoying punishing you for leaving him and the more you plead with him the less likely it will be that you'll be able to get back to him. Indifference on your part and a display of happiness with your new lover is much more likely to get your old boyfriend to want to steal you away — to 'punish' you again.

But this would obviously be a somewhat cynical use of your new boyfriend to further your own ends. This wouldn't be fair on him, especially since he seems to be so kind and considerate. You are not in an easily resolved situation and maybe your best bet would be to get away from both your lovers for a time until you settle down emotionally. It could be that you should seek some psychiatric counselling through your GP in the first instance.

Sad Lad

Dear Ray,

When my mother found out recently that I was gay she was upset but understanding. My father's reaction, on the other hand, was violent to say the least of it. I still live at home because, frankly, I can't afford to get out, but the atmosphere in the household is terrible. Perhaps, at nineteen, I should be ashamed to admit it but I often cry myself to sleep when I go to bed. It isn't as if I'm flaunting a wildly active gay sex life under my father's nose. I don't have a regular boyfriend, so I have no-one to love or to pour my heart out to. All that happened was that, in response to a question about why I wasn't interested in girls that my father thought were attractive, I thought the time was ripe to come out and tell the truth. I said that I'd prefer a male lover. I wish I'd kept my mouth shut.

Callum (Edinburgh)

A mother's love for her son will often transcend the realisation that he is gay. Indeed there are times when some mothers actually feel secretly relieved that they aren't threatened by the possibility of another woman entering their son's life and stealing his love away from them.

On the other hand, fathers tend to expect their sons to demonstrate the same macho mould that they imagine for themselves. A heterosexual father finds the 'insult' of having sired a homosexual child a blow to his masculinity and a difficult psychological cross to bear. Of course there is great injustice, intolerance and lack of understanding in this situation but I'm afraid that we still have a long way to go before society is fully educated into changing its attitudes and behaviour towards homosexuality.

You must try to get your father to understand that you are not throwing down the gauntlet of your gayness before him as a challenge or a threat. You are what you are because it is your nature to be so, not because you have 'decided' to be gay as a kick-in-the-teeth revolt against your parents, their moral standards, or society as a whole. Explain that you need your dad's love and care as much as you ever did — perhaps even more so — and show him that your respect for him remains undiminished. Let him see how upset you are by his rejection of you and enrol your mother's support.

Lazy Lover

Dear Ray,

I'm an active, sexually energetic young man of twenty-two. For the last four years I've been living with the most gorgeous guy in all the universe. He's the same age as I am and he's got a cock on him like a stallion and a beautifully hairy chest. When he's in the mood, bloody hell, can he make love! Next morning I feel like a clapped out Ford Cortina!

But it's that phrase 'when he's in the mood' which is the problem. Weeks go by when he simply isn't interested. He simply tells me to toss myself off, puts out the light and turns over to sleep. I haven't the slightest doubt that he loves me as much as I love him and I have no reason to believe that he is exhausting himself by having it off on the side with anyone else. He's just plain bloody lazy and I'm so frustrated at times I could tear him apart.

Does Spanish Fly work? If so, where can I get some? Or, what about a dozen oysters (though that could come expensive six nights a week!)

Charlie (London)

I don't have much faith in aphrodisiacs — though I'm told that bat's wings sautéed in garlic butter, with frog spawn as a garnish, worked wonders in medieval times!

Perhaps you are going to bed too late, when your boyfriend is very tired after a busy day at work. You know what they say about early to bed, early to 'rise'. You should begin the foreplay even before going to bed, helped by a hot video rather than a hot cocoa! And try him with a bit of his own medicine by playing hard to get on one of the rare occasions when the mood is on him. Remember that alcohol is actually a sexual depressant rather than a stimulant so, while the odd 'nightcap' may help to loosen his inhibitions, even two may be one too many.

Don't forget the value of a straightforward chat about things to bring your frustration out into the open. If he realises that you feel as you do he may make a greater effort to pull his finger (or whatever) out! After four years together he is perhaps beginning to take you for granted. Maybe you can lift him out of his complacency by experimenting with a few new sexual techniques.

Uncircumcised — Should He Tell?

Dear Ray,

I've been courting David, my new boyfriend, for about six months. He's a really wonderful guy in all respects and we are very much in love. We are both ready to buy a house and settle down together, hopefully for the rest of our lives.

I have a major problem, though. You see, David is Jewish and he's circumcised. He has the most beautiful cock I've ever seen — and I've seen lots — and I adore it. I'm not circumcised but the first time we ever made love I had pulled back my foreskin before he realised it and he assumed that I was circumcised too. He whispered to me that he was so glad this was so because he could never have sex with an uncircumcised man.

I can keep my foreskin peeled back quite easily when I've got a hard-on, and for an hour or so afterwards, but gradually it inevitably slips forward again. So far, because we've only been able to have sex in relatively brief sessions either at his parent's home or mine and have never actually slept the night together, I have always managed to hide the fact that I am uncircumcised. But in the future, when we are living together, things are bound to be different. My foreskin won't stay back permanently and I won't be able to avoid him seeing me in my natural state.

I'm quite willing to get myself circumcised. I have the money and I know of a clinic where it can be done but he's bound to see the difference and will obviously find out as soon as we have sex together for the first time afterwards.

I really am 'on the horn' of a dilemma and would appreciate any advice you can give me.

Ken (Croydon)

As you say, I have no doubt that David will find out pretty quickly that you aren't circumcised once you are living together. It would be most unnatural, and virtually impossible, for you to spend the rest of your life hiding your cock from him except when you've got an erection.

Obviously you are faced with two alternatives. Either you come clean with him or you get yourself circumcised without telling him. I don't think there is much point in trying the latter because inevitably he will realise that your cock has changed.

Since that first night when he told you that he couldn't have sex with an uncircumcised man your relationship has blossomed. I think if you now tell him the position he will be fascinated rather than furious and his respect for you will be considerably enhanced when you tell him that you have made appropriate arrangements to be cut. After all, it is a very powerful and positive signal of your love for him that you should take this step.

If David were not to accept that your earlier deceit and subsequent determination to rectify the situation were both reflections of the sincerity of your affection for him, then it would suggest that his love for you is not as soundly based as it ought to be. That would be worrying and perhaps it would be just as well to use this issue as a test of his feelings. It's certainly a matter which must be cleared up before you embark on living together permanently.

Guilty Bisexual

Dear Ray,

I am a forty-six-year-old bisexual man. I have been happily married for twenty-two years and have two sons aged twenty and seventeen.

I have reason to suspect that my wife has recently become aware that I'm having a bit on the side but I think my sons are still ignorant of the fact. My gay life usually consists of one night stands with pub pick-ups or rent boys. Sometimes I take the opportunity during genuine business trips away from home but often I feign work commitments as an excuse to have a night on the tiles. The urge is too strong to give up my gay life. I have tried but invariably yield to the temptation.

My elder son has a girlfriend but I am becoming increasingly worried that my younger son may also have gay tendencies. He has absolutely no interest in girls and has behaved very secretively when asked about one particular male friend of nineteen who has his own flat and from whom he appears quite inseparable. My son often spends the night with the other lad after they've been to rather mysterious parties together.

I'm concerned firstly in case my wife finally revolts and our marriage is threatened and secondly that my younger son is taking after me and will risk putting his life in jeopardy as well.

Martin (Boston, Lincs.)

You don't tell me why you believe that your wife suspects your two-timing, nor do you say whether she has guessed whether it is homo- or hetero- sexual. Clearly, unless you are prepared to come out to her, you have no option but to be extremely careful to avoid further risk of discovery. If you are still enjoying an active sex life with your wife you will have to be doubly certain only to engage in strictly safer sex with your casual male friends. You should also use a condom with your wife, though this may require a bit of difficult explaining if you haven't been using one hitherto. The problems of running with the hare and chasing with the hounds won't just go away. Your battle with your conscience is not one which others can fight for you.

On the other hand, it would be wrong to overdo the guilt with regard to your younger son. As with all growing youngsters he will carve out his own sexual destiny. From what you tell me he doesn't know about your gay activities so there is no reason to believe that he has been influenced by your behaviour. Being gay doesn't put his life 'in jeopardy', provided he handles the issue maturely. Don't be afraid to talk to him about homosexual issues, letting him see your understanding attitude. For all you know he may welcome the opportunity to talk to you about it.

I would be far more worried about his secretive alliance and the mysterious parties if I had the slightest suspicion that they might be drugs-related.

●●●

Inevitably there are many aspects of love which have not been revealed by my choice of letters for this chapter. The 'well of loneliness' is so deep and the bucket can carry just a little of the water, but matters of relationships will emerge in some of the subsequent letters where perhaps some other point is being discussed.

5

I DID IT MY WAY

And now for something different. We all have our funny little ways. A little bit of novelty introduced into the sexual action can enhance the pleasure, or at least give us that little bit of eccentricity which makes our peculiar foibles quite interesting to others. Over the years I've received many letters from guys who do their own thing in their own way. They have their special fantasies and fetishisms and they've written to tell me about them.

Lovely Leather

Dear Ray,
What is it about leather that turns me on? The smell of it is quite exotic and the soft feel of it in my hands is a sensuous delight. Worn next to my skin it sends shivers of excitement up my spine and supple cockstraps made of it give my balls a lovely tight feeling which is really fabulous. Even quite dreary guys cut a much more dashing and manly figure when wearing leathers. It really is great for promoting the macho image.

Bob (Bolton)

Although Bob's letter is rather bland and, in fact, seems to answer its own question, it raises the whole issue of why guys are turned on by either different materials and substances (leather, rubber, velvet, silk, poppers, various foods and drinks — even urine and faeces), or particular physical types or specific sexual practices.

For example, in an earlier chapter I have already referred to the stimulating effect which small pricks and spunk have upon me. I am erect as I write this paragraph which has acted as a trigger to my fantasies. I might add that, for many years, I have shaved my genital area every morning because I love the smooth sensation and the enhanced feeling of close contact with a partner, and believe that it makes hygiene that much easier. I identify very easily with those whose letters follow in which they describe an autoerotic desire to do 'something' to their cocks and balls, such as tattooing or ring insertion, though I have never had the courage to proceed.

Why all this should be so is very hard to explain. I am in danger of falling into a trap about which I have often warned other readers. Amateur psychoanalysis is dangerous; even professional psychoanalysis has its limitations. It is too easy to use hindsight to explain away some feature of today's lifestyle in any individual. It is usually possible to search around wildly in one's past life until one alights upon some feature which can be conveniently used to justify something in the present. You know the kind of thing: 'I don't like big cocks because we always had cucumber sandwiches for tea on Sundays and I don't like cucumber!' This kind of retrospective thinking is a mass of pitfalls but, unfortunately, prospective research is extremely difficult. Do I like small pricks because, being barely over six inches myself, I can remember incidents in my past when I have been intimidated by some bigger guys? I can certainly think of several such occasions. Is my preference for the shaved state related to the fact that I spent several happy twice-a-day years of mess-free masturbation between the age of nine and puberty when I was both smooth and small? Is my fascination with semen something to do with the fact that, in spite of my activity in the field and the physical thrill I could experience in those early years, I actually wasn't able to cum until I was, I guess, nearly seventeen? I was certainly a late developer: the relief of seeing my first ejaculation was enormous. I pose these questions about myself, not really having any confidence in whether, or not, they are relevant to my present preferences. So when readers ask me why they behave in a particular way I may propound a theory but, more often than not, it is somewhat tongue in cheek. I'm much more at home with the idea that — wait for it — it's just the luck of the draw.

Fetishism to do with clothing goes back to the beginning of time with the skins of animals providing man's first form of attire. There is, therefore, something very primitive in the love of leather. What's more, maybe even going back to the uniforms of the Roman legionaries, leather has been associated with the male and macho image. Other materials, silk for example, have a more effeminate connotation. I once heard it said that rubber fetishism had its roots in the latex sap, oozing from the tree, being reminiscent of semen. But I think that's carrying symbolism too far.

Quaint — To Say The Least Of It

Dear Ray,

My actual sex life is very limited. At twenty-seven I have never had sexual intercourse with a man or woman and I only masturbate on rare occasions. I prefer pictures of nude men to women so I guess I'm gay.

What I'm really fascinated by is doing unusual things to my prick and bollocks. I tattooed a dagger on my shaft with a needle and burnt cork when I was thirteen and, since then, my prick and balls have been tattooed professionally on three occasions. I now have nine rings inserted along my cock, including two 'Prince Alberts', and two more large ones — one each side of my balls bag. I am always thinking up new ideas and currently I want nothing more than to have my two balls separated — ie. have the bag slit around the middle and re-stitched as two separate bags hanging side by side. Is this possible and, if so, how would I set about getting it done? Money is no object.

S.P. (Dundee)

I certainly don't know of any surgeon in the UK who would be willing to indulge your fancy, and, in any case, I would have considerable reservations about supporting you. However, it is practical as I can testify from personal witness and from many photos of this and other bizarre genital mutilations. I'm told that the centre of such surgical activities is Casablanca.

You would certainly have a conversation stopper between your legs — but who would see it in the absence of any active sex life? I should warn you against such totally introverted narcissism/masochism. You really need to develop a broader based, socially interactive lifestyle and, hopefully, a more satisfying shared sex life.

And For My Next Trick

Dear Ray,

My sex life is very limited. At forty I've only ever been fucked by two or three men, and I prefer photographs of nude men to women because women don't have cocks. I am really fascinated by doing unusual things to my cock and balls. Ever since my pubic hair started to grow at the age of thirteen I shaved it off and have now got rid of most of it permanently by electrolysis. I've had my balls tattooed but not, so far, my cock itself, though I suspect it won't be long before I do. I have thirteen rings inserted around the centre line of my balls, plus another between my balls and my arse and yet another two at each side of the base of my cock. I have three further rings in my cockhead, inserted through my pisshole. Also, I used to have a

'Prince Albert' piercing just below the rim on the underside of my cock but this hole has now been cut away since I had it joined up with my pisshole: I've been getting the slit enlarged in turn upwards and downwards and can now open the hole very wide indeed. I find that stroking the sensitive inner skin is quite a turn on for me. I need the three rings described above to keep the two flaps closed. At some later stage I envisage getting a new 'Prince Albert' piercing further down the shaft to make up for the one I lost.

Eddie (Suffolk)

Before readers think that you are taking the piss, and expecting me to believe an exaggerated fantasy, may I say that I know you well. We have corresponded over several years and I have personally photographed your 'paraphernalia'. May I also explain, for those who are not into the finer points of piercing and infibulation, that a 'Prince Albert' involves inserting a ring through the natural urethral opening at the tip of the glans and causing it to re-emerge through a hole in the undersurface of the penis approximately one centimetre behind the natural opening. A more mutilating variation of this, a 'Queen Victoria', brings the ring out through an opening in the top of the penis either through the flesh of the glans itself or immediately behind the corona (rim).

Jingle Balls

Dear Ray,
    Like Eddie, I'm very much into body piercing. So far I've got three separate piercings in each nipple, twelve in my foreskin, one large hole taking eleven rings through my glans, two in my frenum, two on the

shaft and forty piercings in my ballsbag. This isn't a wishful boast. I've got photos to prove it.

Do you know if there is a record for the number of piercings on one person?

'Ring-a-Ding-Ding' (Hants)

How very strange! I've studied every page of the Guinness Book of Records and that's about the only one that isn't there! I've seen your photographs to confirm your claim and suggest you send them to the publishers — which will probably make them think that they've been drinking too much of their own brew!

Nipple Ring Cover-Up (1)

Dear Ray,

I have been interested in recent HIM correspondence about sexual piercings of genitalia and nipples. I wonder if this is something peculiar to the... um, 'peculiar'? Obviously such piercings are strongly autoerotic and it is interesting that most of your correspondents make the point that their partnered sex life appears to be deficient.

I have nipple rings and my problem is that even the smallest ring is visible through the sweat shirt I wear to work and this causes me embarrassment. If I leave the rings out during the daytime the holes close up so quickly. Apart from a Band-Aid have you any suggestions for a cover-up?

Mike (Banbury)

Infibulation of ears, nose, lips, nipples, male and female genitalia has been a form of body decoration for centuries and is most certainly not confined to the... um, 'peculiar'! Clearly, piercing the more intimate parts of the body has a more strongly erotic significance than, say, earrings, but the emphasis should be on the 'auto-erotic' and not the 'homo-erotic'. Gender doesn't seem to matter. Apart from wearing a bra I'm a bit stuck for ways of concealing your 'titillation'. Let's see if readers have any ideas.

Nipple Ring Cover-Up (2)

Dear Ray,

There are two answers to the problem of keeping open nipple piercings while wearing a see-through shirt.

One is to use a short strand of colourless nylon, as is often found on price tags, which will remain in place unnoticed and has the added attraction of occasionally catching on the fabric of the shirt, thus providing a mild thrill.

The second method is to thread double thickness cotton of the same colour as the nipple through the hole with a blunt needle. The cotton should be soaked in antiseptic to avoid the introduction of infection and can be trimmed to the right length.

Paul (Exmouth)

All this talk of nipples lead to a very apologetic letter which didn't even begin 'Dear Ray'...

Nibbled Nipples

Sir,

Please forgive me this indiscipline, but I had assumed that a master more qualified than I, a mere slave, would have wished to discuss the question of improving one's nipples. I used to suffer from small, untrained nipples but, under the supervision of my master, these improved to such an extent that he felt able to exhibit me frequently.

Nipples require frequent, regular attention to be maintained in peak condition. Perhaps you will allow me to recite the methods I was trained to use. My master instructed me to shave the area above my pectorals and keep it free of hair. I was beaten if I failed and since I was also required to keep my cock, balls and anus hairfree, these beatings were not infrequent at first.

I was instructed to massage each nipple with surgical spirit twice daily for seven days after which I was made to brush each nipple with a stiff hairbrush for a minimum of five minutes, building up to thirty minutes daily. Although painful my master explained that this was to make me aware of my nipples and, after about a month of this treatment, I discovered that merely by touching them I would achieve a strong erection. Thereafter my master gave them his personal attention using his teeth, but always refusing to allow me to cum though the desire was intense.

He subsequently pierced both my nipples and a further stage of the development has been the wearing of clamps and tit weights. The climax of my master's achievement was when I was brought before a group of his friends and was required to bring myself off purely by working on my own tits.

Robert (Hants)

I have abridged your letter since it first appeared in HIM because it was then very explicit with regard to some of your master's more bizarre activities with you and a subsequent court case caused me some concern as to whether it would be wise to publish details of such goings on. As it is, I suspect that your public performance of autoerotic nipple stimulation leading to orgasm is legally a bit 'iffy'.

Your letter is interesting, though, in that it highlights not only nipple sensitivity as a source of sexual gratification but also the importance of masochism to some people as a means to the same end.

Let's move on to something a little less hairy...

Smooth Is Beautiful

Dear Ray,

Is it common for people to enjoy shaving their bodies? It's a fetish I've enjoyed for a couple of years now though I've never shaved anyone else or had them do it to me. I thoroughly enjoy the smoothness and the hygiene it brings.

In the magazines I've only seen a few nude models with shaved bodies and wish there were more of them. I believe shaving is quite common amongst swimmers, weightlifters, musclemen and wrestlers. I do not ally it to the S & M scene, but I believe many do.

Ken (Basingstoke)

Smooth swimmers move faster through the water. Smooth wrestlers avoid getting their hair pulled. Smooth muscle-men can show off their muscles to better advantage. These are not examples of sexual fetishism. They are practical requirements and any sexual titillation must be primarily in the eye of the beholder.

I don't ally shaving with the S & M scene either, but those who do will say that hirsutism, the possession of thick body hair, is strongly in the macho image and the shaven state thus projects the opposite concept of slave submission and a willingness to be dominated.

I think it is true that the shaved body 'softens' a guy's 'maleness', but it should not be construed as effeminate. I have written above of my own preferences in this field but I certainly see myself very much in the masculine mould and, to me, the whole ethos of my homosexuality is my preference for men. I very definitely want my men to be men.

Since your letter first appeared in an early HIM there has been most definitely an upsurge in the popularity of genital shaving amongst gay men. I suspect that it has something to do with a greater awareness of the need for safer sex in the wake of AIDS and is part of the general upsurge in auto-erotic (DIY) sexual activities which has occurred.

Hairy Holocaust

> Dear Ray,
> Talking about shaving the most intimate parts, I've been doing this for years. I would clearly like to get rid of these ugly hairs forever and have heard of the process called electrolysis. Could you tell me more about it, please?
>
> Anon. (Brighton)

A 'please' at last! Is yours the first letter in this book in which this little word has appeared? Maybe not, but, sad to say, I don't read it very often — and even more sadly I rarely get any follow-up letters which say 'thank you' or give me the feedback I need to evaluate the worth, or otherwise, of some of my suggestions... but that's just me getting my oar in!

As for electrolysis, this is a procedure which is quite expensive and very slow when undertaken by one of the specialist hair removal clinics. Quite apart from causing a few raised eyebrows if you were to attend to seek permanent removal of your pubic hair, it would involve many visits. The hair roots are killed one by one by introducing an electrical discharge with a small needle through each hair follicle and that means a lot of work to destroy the whole of your pubic mat. Do It Yourself electrolysis kits are now fairly widely available, especially through mail order outlets, but be warned: it will take a long time and will need great perseverance.

A word of warning. One of my correspondents tried using one of the depilatory (hair removing) creams and burnt his skin sufficiently badly to need hospital treatment. The skin 'down there' is more sensitive than elsewhere on the body so do be careful if you experiment with any of these products.

Kinky Curlies

Dear Ray,

From time to time you have asked readers to tell you what turns us on. How about this?

Many years ago a former lover was going overseas. With great solemnity he presented me with a lock of his pubic hair in a cellophane package as a keepsake. It started me off on a collection which now exceeds seven hundred packets, all carefully stored in a set of trays originally designed for a butterfly collection. They are divided into two sections — those I've slept with, and those I haven't. You'd be surprised how many gay celebrities, on request, have sent me a lock together with their autograph. One of the fascinating aspects is the difference in the colour of the hair on their head and on their balls.

I spend hours arranging and re-arranging my collection, fantasising while I am doing so. The real challenge is writing to guys asking them to add an item and, when I persuade some of the most unexpected people to join in, it is a fantastic turn-on. Now it's your turn to join the Hall of Fame and I'm writing to ask you for a tuft.

It's a great hobby and adds new meaning to the phrase 'being grabbed by the short and curlies'.

Toby (Salford)

I'm honoured — I think! Whatever next? Is there some guy out there collecting pickled foreskins?

As I'm a pubic shaver you'll have to wait until I let a restricted area grow especially for you — but other readers be warned, I'm definitely not in the game of growing to order! Well, almost definitely. I might just agree to the odd tangle at £50 a grow! Much better than shyness, that really could be a 'saleable product'.

Combing Out!

Dear Ray,

I like the idea of letting my pubic hair grow until it forms a long flowing beard. I have a really great pubic bush of gingery hair though the hair on my head is dark brown. I can just imagine the talking point it would be if every time I pulled my trousers down I could flaunt long locks of hair almost down to my knees.

Unfortunately, though I can grip a single hair and perhaps stretch it out to as long as four or five inches, as soon as I leave go it springs back into its little curly coil. I've tried combing my hair when it's wet; I've tried trying to straighten it with various chemicals, and I've even tried to 'perm' it straight rather than curly, but all to no avail. So I was wondering whether you have any suggestions to help me achieve my objective.

By the way, I'm twenty-two years old and I wouldn't miss your column for all the hair on Samson's head.

Steven (Exeter).

I must say that I like the idea. This is the first time in twenty years that I recall being asked this particular question, so you've scored a first on that point. And I'm not immune to flattery so thanks for the compliment: I'm no Samson and I'm fast losing the remains of my top cover.

Sadly, I have to tell you that your idea is a virtual non-starter. Our pubic hair is genetically incapable of growing to any great length, just in the same way as the tangled mat on a negro's head will always regrow in tight curls no matter what efforts he might make to straighten it.

The hair which grows on our body is controlled by different genes from that which grows on our head and that's why it has different characteristics of curliness, length and colour. I can contemplate changing the hair growth pattern in controlled experiments on animals (such as selectively breeding certain sheep to provide a good wool yield), but to attempt some grandiose programme of selective breeding through several generations of humans to favour long, straight pubic hair is a bit of a tall order.

Straight As A Die

Dear Ray,

I loved reading the letter from Steven of Exeter in which he expressed a desire to grow straight pubic hair.

My problem is that my pubes are completely straight. All my sexual partners have remarked on this and it has become something of a mild embarrassment to me, though certainly something to talk about. So far I have not seen anyone else in my category. Is this due to a genetic mutation or abnormality? I am also interested to know whether there are any links between straight pubic hair and difficulty in sustaining an erection during penetrative sex.

By the way, I'm thirty and my straight pubic hair is the only 'straight' thing about my sex life.

Brian (Huddersfield)

I have no idea why you should be so 'straight-laced'. Yes, it's certainly genetic but I can't promise you that if you pull down your dad's knickers you'll find him to be the same. Who knows where the un-bent gene lies? But you don't need to use the word 'abnormality' — 'variation on a theme' might be more appropriate. There's not much you can do about it, unless you fancy trying a home perm.

I can assure you, however, that it has nothing to do with problems of keeping a 'stiffie' while set to screw. You don't precisely pin-point that problem to yourself but I am putting two and two together and assuming that it is you who has some difficulty along these lines.

It isn't for me to interfere with your love life, though I do hope you take precautions and use a condom. Yours isn't an unusual problem — a lot of folk complain of going 'off the boil' just at the crucial moment. It is usually because of some hidden, deep-down fear (perhaps of something like AIDS) or a guilt reaction to the morality which, no doubt, you had impressed upon you as you grew up. These can be very deep rooted and hard to overcome but it helps if you have a lot of foreplay, if necessary with help from mags or videos, to get you absolutely steaming and rock hard ready to go before you begin to poke. Use plenty of lubrication and get your partner utterly relaxed first so that you can slip in quickly and easily without too much 'fumbling with your key in the lock'.

And now for something close to the dicks of all of us...

Custer's Last Stand

Dear Ray,
    My cock and I have decided that we will not yield
to the present boxer shorts revolution! I'd prefer my
prick to be standing up for its rights, held firmly
against my abdominal wall by my snug fitting briefs,
rather than to be swinging low in the sweet chariot of
support-free underwear.
    That, 'briefly', is what this letter is all about.
Boxers may be OK to let the wind out when you fart
but otherwise they're the biggest let-down since the
warm water leaked out of my Jac-Pac.
    What is your view?

Keith (Derby)

My view depends upon what I'm looking at. There are times
when bollocks in boxers look better than buttocks in briefs. I
suppose that there are those who believe that making a
holocaust of their briefs is a man's stand for freedom in a
Women's Lib world of bra-burning females. Personally I
prefer my stand to be a little less free. I enjoy the control
which I exercise over my dick by the combination of a
cockstrap and flesh-hugging briefs — preferably one size
smaller than I ought to wear for decency.
    When briefs first became popular the prophets of doom
anticipated that man's fertility would suffer horrendously as
his balls were held too warmly against his body and denied
their natural freedom to swing but, in the event, the condom
and the pill have proved far more efficient contraceptives.
    True, boxers provide a larger area upon which to print
outrageously camp pictures and grafitti, but you don't need
a lot of space to draw attention to 'Custer's Last Stand'.

More On Briefs Vs. Boxers

Dear Ray,

I agree with Keith of Derby that I like to see a well
supported crotch in a tight pair of jeans and it's those
snug-fitting briefs that lift the vital parts. However, I
have to admit that I like to have my cock and balls
hang free and, as the fashion these days is for baggy
trousers, I favour boxer shorts.

Pete (Darlington)

Dear Ray,

Boxers or briefs? After seeing some young men
strip to their boxers and how pretty they were — one
pair looked like white satin with little red hearts on
— I decided to try these. But what a let-down! How
uncomfortable they were! For me it's the small slips
every time. I find thongs to be very comfortable.
Whatever you wear you should hold what you've got
in place without obstructing the view.

Tim (Henley)

That's enough on that topic. 'Yer pays yer money and yer
takes yer pick!'

Here's a motley assortment of letters with which to round
off this chapter.

Footsie

Dear Ray,

I wonder how many of your readers share my
harmless interest in feet. I don't mean imperial
measurement. I mean the flat bits that prevent your

legs from fraying.

My interest is hard to explain. I'm not especially masochistic and I have no way-out desires to be kicked to death or walked on. I just love to see a good-looking guy either in stockinged or bare feet. Mind you, like everyone else I also like to see the 'naughty bits', so I suppose my foot fetish is something of a bonus. What a pity, though, that gay mags nearly always cut their models off at the ankles.

I can hardly explain the thrill I get from watching unsuspecting young men strolling along the beach barefooted. If only they knew they would be far less happy to exhibit their more intimate parts. The thrill Victorian gentlemen used to experience when long-skirted ladies revealed an inch of ankle intrigues me. Has my fetish similar roots?

Philip (Huddersfield)

Baldilocks And The Three Hairs

Dear Ray,

Some of your readers talk about how sexy they find it to have their feet stroked, others say their nipples are very sensitive. Have you ever heard of anyone who can cum his load (look, no hands!) just as soon as someone begins to stroke the big bald patch on the top of his head?

My hair began to recede before I was twenty-one and I got very uptight about it. By the time I was twenty-four I was as bald as a coot except at the sides. I was desperate. I spent a fortune on toupees, but they always looked stupid and they were a waste of time because my rate of balding outstripped one after another. I really thought I was on the shelf and would never find another lover.

Then one day a guy picked me up in a cottage — I swear the lights were so dim he couldn't see I was bald — and when we got home and stripped off he began to stroke the top of my head very gently. I've never developed an erection so quickly and before I knew what was happening I'd cum.

The top of my head remains intensely sensitive and my party trick is to bring myself off just by lightly stroking it.

Neil (Cumbernauld)

Cockstrap Blues

Dear Ray,

For me there's nothing like wearing a really tight cockstrap when I wank. My cock goes dark blue with engorgement of blood and the veins stand out prominently as if they are about to burst. It makes me feel all man!

If I put the strap on as tight as I can even when I'm really soft the constriction is out of this world when I get a hard-on; the only trouble is that when I reach orgasm, although everything feels as if it is about to explode, no spunk can actually squeeze past the barrier. Where does it go to and do you think anything could go wrong to spoil my enjoyment.

Mark (Halifax)

Most of the above group of letters are self-explanatory and I don't need to reproduce the replies which I wrote in HIM. However, Mark's letter gives me a peg to hang on a few comments about cockstraps in general.

When I first became aware of cockstraps on sale in the newly opened sex shops back in the sixties, I was very sceptical about them but, having been given several in various shapes and sizes to try and comment on I must say that I soon became quite addicted to them. The simplest straps, or rings of metal, either form a tight constriction behind the base of the cockshaft and balls, or a collar around

121

the neck of the scrotum, or both. I personally favour a leather strap with an easily released pop-stud so that, if it becomes too tight, it can be released quickly. Although purpose-made straps and rings can be quite expensive, cheap alternatives can be made out of everyday objects like kitten collars, stationery rings and shower curtain rings.

The constriction to the blood flow in the penis created by a base strap leads to a well-maintained firm erection but Mark is taking risks by wearing one that is too tight. Blood vessels could burst in exactly the way he feels that they are going to and this could cause severe bruising and even permanent scarring to the tissues of the penis.

Within reason, though, the sensation is great. The strap gives the flaccid cock a very comforting sensation of 'uplift' and creates a constant state of slight arousal which is an enjoyable background accompaniment as one goes about the chores of daily living. During erection, because the base of the penis is kept narrow by the constraining ring, the whole organ bends very easily in all directions at its root and is thus much more easily manipulated into 'dark passageways'.

The scrotal collar strap holds the testicles low in the scrotum, giving an enhanced crotch outline in tight trousers. More important, it prevents them from rising as orgasm approaches. The natural rise of your balls at this time is nature's way of protecting them against the bashing they might otherwise get against your partner's body if they were swinging free while you bonk. The muscle pull involved is an integral part of the thrill of orgasm. Anything which makes those muscles pull harder enhances the sensation of the climax and, of course, they must pull harder in a vain attempt to overcome the constriction of the ring.

In Mark's case, because his cock base strap is so tight, his spunk cannot move forwards through the urethra (the pipe along the penis). It has only one alternative, to force its way backwards through the muscle ring which guards the entrance into and out of the bladder. Inside, as the bladder fills up with urine, the spunk is gradually diluted and it will eventually pass out to the exterior when he has a pee. He may, or may not, notice a slight cloudiness of his urine, but that's all.

A rarely used form of birth control, known as the Saxoni-cus method, involves applying strong pressure on the under surface of the base of the penis at the time of ejaculation. Although this is done with the fingers the effect is the same as with the tight cockstrap. It has been suggested that repeated back pressure on the bladder sphincter muscles may weaken them, possibly leading to incontinence in old age. I wouldn't like to be certain of this risk but I can imagine that all the various pressures that are built up by a cockstrap or ring which is too tight could easily put a strain on the whole reproductive tract. On balance, I think Mark would be wiser to avoid his over-tight Cockstrap Blues! A comfortable strap is great but he shouldn't strangle his dick.

TV Tendency

Dear Ray,

I am conscious of increasing transvestite tenden-cies. It started off as simply a fascination for the feeling of silk against my skin so I used to buy silk underwear. That led on to wearing ladies' tights and now, at twenty-four, I spend quite a lot of time when my parents are out dressing up in my mother's clothes and wanking off in front of the bedroom mirror.

Yet I have a very manly, well-built hairy body and I don't feel effeminate. In fact my supreme fantasy is to be dressed as an immaculate tart, pick up an unsuspecting punter and then reveal myself as a really macho male, giving him the thrill of a lifetime — thus proving the superiority of homosexuality over heterosexuality.

Is all this normal, or should I be worried? Where will it end?

Bill (Watford)

In a way, normality, like beauty, is in the eye of the beholder. It depends very largely upon the attitude of the person who is assessing the behaviour. There are limits, of course. I don't think anyone, other than the guy who is doing it, would say that child murder in the interests of sexual gratification is normal. However, if you believe that sex is purely for the procreation of children, then 'normality' must be strictly limited to heterosexual intercourse with that objective in mind. If, on the other hand, you believe that sex is also for enjoyment and fulfilling a meaningful relationship, regardless of gender, then 'normality' is much wider. It is easy enough to carry this just a small stage further and say that the fun element of sex can be enlivened, perfectly normally, by adding a little novelty to the action.

So long as you don't spend too much time admiring yourself in front of the mirror, when you could be out finding a partner, what you are doing is a perfectly harmless way of adding a bit of spice to your masturbation.

One-Off Fetish

Dear Ray,

I'm twenty-six and I've been gay since I was thirteen. I have a weird fetish which really turns me on. For as long as I can remember I've got a real hard on whenever I've seen a one-legged man walking down the street. I'll go miles out of my way to follow him. Over the years I've managed to make a collection of one-legged guys' photographs from newspapers and magazines and I get a tremendous thrill looking at these while I'm wanking.

Am I alone in this field?

Tony (Bath)

Although your fetish is certainly 'one-off', in one sense you are far from being alone in your peculiarity. There are quite often adverts in the gay personal columns for amputee partners, and there is a flourishing Gay Men's Limbless Group based in Epping in Essex.

So long as you respect the equality of a one-legged partner as an individual and don't try to be patronising or irritatingly hyper-sympathetic, you have nothing to worry about and nor does any suitable partner who comes your way. Good luck to you.

And this one has to be the last...

Nail-Biting

> Dear Ray,
> Here's another unusual fetish to add to your collection. Although I have an almost perfect manicure and am therefore unable to bite my own nails, there's nothing I like better than to bite a guy's nails until they are red raw. I find sucking their bitten fingers a tremendous turn-on. I'm twenty-eight and for the past ten years I've been obsessed with guys who chew their finger nails right down to the quick.
>
> Rob (Maidenhead)

A psychologist friend of mine came up with the suggestion that your pleasure in sucking a nail-bitten finger may be linked with a preference for circumcised cocks, either in your partner or reflecting a secret yearning of your own if you are not circumcised.

●●●

Four years of HIM have produced such a fascinating wealth of material that I find it hard to stop, but we must move on.

6

WE DID IT OUR WAY

In the last chapter and again in this one I have interpreted the words 'fetish', 'fantasy', 'eccentricity', and perhaps a few others that the thesaurus could throw up, very loosely to enable me to bring together the letters which highlight the less than usual attitudes and behaviour associated with gay sex. We have seen some of these in relation to those who are primarily 'solo operators'. Now let's move on to what, for want of a better name, can be called 'the partnered unusual'. I'm carefully avoiding the word 'kinky', because that may imply something which is rather bizarre, or even 'abnormal'.

Fortunately HIM readers, by and large, are a fairly sane section of the gay community. Maybe, from time to time, some of their activities are a bit way out but I rarely receive any letters which go really over the top into the realms of the utterly crazy.

The horizons of sexual behaviour are forever being pushed outwards in the search for even bigger, wilder, orgasmic thrills. I've seen a lot of changes over the years of my gay life. Many of yesterday's 'perversions' are more or less accepted as commonplace today. Who knows what parts of today's outer fringe activities will be seen as run of the mill by the turn of the century?

I spent a couple of years 'on the game' in my late teens. That was away back in 1951 and '52. In those days nobody had heard of fist-fucking or water sports, and dildoes, vibrators, butt plugs, cockstraps and the like were all still waiting to be invented.

I suppose one of the most alarming letters I ever received is printed below. My concern surrounded the stupidity of the behaviour and the enthusiastic way it was described. Fortunately, letters such as this one are few and far between.

'No, No — A Thousand Times NO'

Dear Ray,

Try this one for size. I really wanted to get my spunk inside my lover. Really inside, I mean, not just up his arse or over his tonsils. It would be truly symbolic of our love if we could exchange our sperm in a way that it couldn't get out... so...

We got one of those 'bendy straws' which the kids like to drink through and KYed both ends. There's a sort of corrugated bit about one third of the way along which allows it to bend freely. Very gently I eased the shorter end up the tube of my prick then, standing close together, we eased the longer end up his cock, just like a doctor passing a catheter. We were surprised how easily we could manage it. By now we were both very excited and it only needed a couple of light pulls to make me cum. It passed along the straw and went right up inside him. I don't think we spilled a drop.

We removed the tube and, after about ten minutes, reinserted it the other way. This time it was his turn to cum into me. It was an incredible sensation to feel my prick filling up with his sperm. We now feel that we have fully consummated our union.

What do you say to that?

Bri-John (Southampton)

How bloody stupid can you get? I only print your letter to show other readers the imbecilic tricks that two fools like you can get up to. Talk about taking risks of seriously damaging your urethras or of introducing infections... The mind boggles!

What do I say to that? No, No, a thousand times no!

Here's a less frightening shared fantasy...

Role Play

Dear Ray,

Before we met, my partner and I had our own recurrent wanking fantasies which played quite an important part in our mainly DIY sexual activities.

I always imagined myself as a patient who was being examined by a doctor. The detail of the fantasy would vary. Sometimes I'd be the victim of an accident with an injured prick or perhaps a psychiatrist would seduce me (or I would seduce him) while I was lying on his couch. The options were legion, but the patient/doctor theme was always in the background.

When my partner came along — we met totally by accident, getting into conversation when we were sitting next to each other in a theatre — it turned out that he always fantasised himself into the role of doctor in all sorts of scenarios similar to my own. Actually, his fantasising was even more sophisticated than mine. He had actually fitted out a 'doctor's surgery' and single-bed 'hospital ward' at his home. Here he would play out his fantasies either on his own or, sometimes, with a casual pick-up. 'Doctor' and 'patient' would end up in bed together and then the 'treatment' would begin.

We don't live together, but I've been visiting him two or three times a week for over a year now. It's a perfect match. We never tire of exploring new sexual avenues in our role play and sex sessions.

Now to the problem. Neither one of us has any ties and there is no real reason why we shouldn't live together. He wants me to give up my bed-sitter and move into his bigger, and appropriately fitted out, flat. But, for me, half the fun is 'going to see the doctor', and wondering what he might have in store for me. The whole fantasy may collapse if I move in and the doctor/patient relationship is undermined.

I have this awful feeling that if we were under the same roof all the time I could no longer think of him as my 'doctor' and I'd no longer be able to provide 'spunk specimens' for him to send off to the 'laboratory' for analysis!

Noel (Gloucester)

You are both enjoying a sexually fulfilling relationship based very firmly on the accidental coming together of two highly compatible erotic fantasies. Generally speaking, the power of fantasy is a valuable contributor to solo or shared sex play. Occasionally, however, as you are probably aware, it can get out of hand and some pretty violent tragedies have occurred when some guys have been carried too deeply into their fantasy world.

I assume that you are both sensible enough not to carry your fantasies to extremes but you are still faced with another dilemma of which I think you are already becoming conscious. It seems that you may have become excessively dependent upon the content of your fantasies to achieve sexual satisfaction. In spite of the variations on the theme, the emphasis on the separate doctor and patient roles is actually beginning to push you apart rather than pull you together. Moving in with each other will only work if you are truly socially compatible beyond the stethoscope and bedpan world of your fantasies.

I suggest that you concentrate on widening your non-sexual social activities together and see how you get on in the fuller sense. You have already identified the possible pitfalls of your present somewhat restrictive sexual repertoire.

Well, Fantasy That!

Dear Ray,

I guess that, like most guys, I enjoy sexual fantasies when I'm having a wank. I'm pretty good at it and my mind is really carried away so that I almost believe that I actually am with my regular lover, even though he lives fifty miles away.

The trouble is that the fantasy is actually becoming better than the real thing. I really go wild when I'm drooling in my imagination what Jack and I are going to do together when we next get together. I pump away harder and harder and, in due course, reach a king size orgasm which splatters the spunk around the place like the Trafalgar Square fountains.

Then, when Jack arrives and we go to bed together it isn't half so good. Indeed, the last time he came over it was an absolute disaster. I couldn't cum at all and he went home in a huff saying that I must have been with some other guy earlier in the day. But as soon as he'd gone I started to think about him and, lo and behold, out spewed the semen with gay abandon.

What's the answer? Obviously Jack means a hell of a lot to me or I couldn't think about him the way I do, but I'm afraid I'll lose him if I don't perform better in his arms.

Victor (Plymouth)

The power of fantasy can be very strong and is usually a healthy way of improving the quality of masturbation. However, you have highlighted a danger which is always present when the object of the fantasy is too close and similar to real life expectations of partnered sex. Imagination knows no bounds but sex with a partner is constrained by the limits of practicality and so can prove less satisfactory than fantasising about the same partner.

As a twice-a-day wanker I, too, have developed a powerful ability to fantasise, but I try to concentrate on wildly extravagant scenarios which could never occur in real life. For example, as a semen freak, a mind-blowing recurring theme of mine is to go swimming in a pool of the stuff produced by an army of naked, masturbating marines. This is so far removed from credibility in a real life situation that it in no way interferes with the action when I'm actually in bed with a lover.

Concentrate on developing a way-out fantasy and see if it helps.

Bow-Wow-TV

Dear Ray,
   Are there any advantages/disadvantages in face to face anal intercourse when compared to rear entry doggy fashion?

Mike (Bristol)

What a good question. I don't suppose that anybody has ever really researched the issue and, quite seriously, there could be significant differences. If your partner has an upward curving penis then I would think that, from an anatomical point of view, the face to face position would allow him to stimulate your prostate gland through the wall of your rectum more satisfactorily. Most people, however, seem to find that gaining entry from behind is easier and this might result in less risk of injury to the lining of your rectum. To do it either way properly, without causing one's partner pain or injury, requires quite considerable technical skill and my guess is that the difference isn't significant. For a good fuck what really matters is the experience of both participants (active and passive), and some guys will be better at it one way and some the other.

Of course, there's absolutely no doubt that doggy fashion is much easier if you both want to watch TV while you're doing it.

Training

Dear Ray,

I'd do anything for my boyfriend. Well, almost anything! It is sheer ecstasy when he rims me but I simply couldn't bring myself to do it to him in return. I didn't mind sucking him right off, and didn't mind the taste of his cum (I still don't), but rimming was more than I could face. Yet I did so desperately want to give him a good time.

Then he hit upon an idea: flavoured rimming! Before we go to bed he goes down to the kitchen and liberally smears some pleasant flavour in his crack — maybe honey or golden syrup or chocolate spread, jam or even Marmite. It has worked wonders. I think to myself, 'What is he using tonight?' and I just can't wait to get my tongue down there to find out. It really is excellent training because now I can do it without any fears even when he isn't using anything.

Dave (East Grinstead)

I think this letter is fun and will make it easier for guys who are reluctant rimmers to cope with the situation. I know rimming is a very popular sexual technique and, as far as AIDS is concerned, probably not very hazardous. However, I shall have more to say later on about the several other dangers of this practice so, at this stage, let's just say that I have included your letter somewhat 'tongue in cheek'!

I have fewer reservations about this next letter which is on a similar theme.

A Taste Of Honey

Dear Ray,

My boyfriend and I frequently enjoy oral sex. We sixty-nine regularly and usually swallow each other's spunk when we cum. I know there are some guys who think that this is quite disgusting, but, I'm sorry, that's the way we do it and we don't feel guilty or ashamed about it.

The only problem is that I find my fella's spunk very bitter. I've been swallowing the cum of different guys for years but I've never tasted anything quite like his. It sends quite a shiver through my body when I receive his load.

I find that if I take a tablespoon of thick honey and swish it around my mouth before the action begins the flavour lingers long enough to counteract the bitterness of his spunk. I'm writing to you not so much because I have a problem but because I have found a solution which some other readers, perhaps too embarrassed to write about the matter, will welcome so that they can more fully enjoy their own cock-sucking experiences.

Alan (Powys)

I'm including your letter for two reasons. Firstly, because I know only too well that the flavour of spunk can vary considerably from one guy to the next and it is, as you say, sometimes very bitter. Your solution, though probably not new to many experienced cock suckers, is worth drawing to the attention of some who are perhaps new to the art and less well informed.

The second reason for printing your letter is because, contrary to your assertion that you are not guilty or ashamed, I believe that you are. You are far too apologetic when you comment that some guys probably think oral sex, to ejaculation and swallowing, is disgusting. Maybe you are right in believing that some guys do, in fact, believe this to be the case but cock-sucking is one of the most common of all gay sexual techniques. What's more it is in a 'low risk' category as far as the spread of HIV infection is concerned. Many thousands of orgasms are achieved this way every day. You have no need to think that you have to justify your activities as if you are indulging in something outside normal gay experience.

The More The Merrier?

Dear Ray,

As a schoolboy I rapidly exhausted all the kicks I could create for myself with ordinary solo masturbation techniques. I soon moved on to partnered sex and had several affairs which ran their course and taught me practically every possible way of coming off with another guy. Once again I reached the stage where new bedmates presented no challenge. Nothing different ever happened. I'd done it all before.

Then, six months ago I became involved in my first threesome. Wow! This was really all singing, all dancing stuff!! It was too good to last, and last it didn't. Three spunk-shooting dicks in harmony eventually began to put even that fire out. Now I'm into mighty, multiple orgies — the more the merrier — on a great big polythene sheet with loads of slippery, slithery baby oil, poppers in abundance and absolutely no holds barred.

What I want to know is where do I go next?

Rob (Bristol)

You'll probably go to prison if you're not careful. Remember, the law only allows two men over the age of twenty-one to have sex together in private. Three or more is a breach of the rules. Orgies, I'm afraid, are out. You have been warned.

Perhaps you'd be better off if you took a few steps backward and looked for a bit of 'love' rather than 'lust' in your life. A single partnership, based on mutual affection, may give you both long-lasting satisfaction.

Plugging The Butt

Dear Ray,

Are butt plugs medically safe? My partner wants me to buy one and has asked me to let him use it in our love-making. I'm not keen. Even the catalogue pictures — like a black Zeppelin — alarm me. I've never had any penetrative anal sex experience and I don't think I'm psychologically or physically ready for what my partner wants. Nor do I think that our very close relationship has need of sex technology to help it along. His interest in anal sex is new and he is now accusing me of not really loving him because I won't go along with it. We've had some sharp rows as a result.

It is ridiculous that an imitation plastic cock should come between us to spoil an otherwise very happy relationship. I don't like the idea of anal sex and the possibility of internal damage by a butt plug makes me shudder.

We've been together for a full year and, naturally, I want to please him but I can only agree to what he wants when I am assured that other couples use sex toys with no danger to their bodies. I won't enquire whether there is any pleasure to be got from receiving a butt plug because I'm convinced there is none.

David (Cambridge)

It seems that your lover doesn't share your opinion that your relationship doesn't need sex technology to help it along. His insistence suggests that he isn't very sensitive to your wishes in the matter. If you've never had any anal experience what is there in it for him if you use a butt plug? I suspect an element of sadism on his part, and that doesn't augur well for the long-term future of your togetherness.

Butt plugs come in a variety of sizes and, if you were to yield to his pressure, you would have to insist on starting with the smallest size which would have to be very well lubricated before even trying to insert it. Until you've learnt to relax it isn't easy to accept a butt plug. You'd be better off starting with a fairly small rubber artificial cock or dildo. A plug is intended for fairly long insertion and 'locks' into place, but it is only likely to give pleasure if you like that sort of thing.

Of course there is a potential for injury and, if you are not attracted to the idea, then you must be firm and say, 'No.'

●●●

A very serious subject which must be included in a book of this kind, but which needs to be tackled with great care, is that of the effects of child abuse. The very word 'paedophilia' is charged with emotion and passion these days and I think the following letter provides an interesting point of view.

Child Sexual Abuse

Dear Ray,

Many abused children apparently do not suffer long-term psychological or physical damage. Others clearly do. May I relate the circumstances of myself and my brother?

I am the elder, now thirty-one, and my brother is only fourteen months younger. We were very close as children and always shared the same bedroom. I

remember when I was thirteen and he was twelve we
found a book that talked about masturbation and
read it in bed one night by torchlight. We both tried it
that night for the first time and both had orgasms
though only I produced a drop or two of rather watery
spunk.

Not long after, on a trip to the seaside, we got
talking to a man of about thirty-five who invited us
into his private beach hut. We went in in all innocence but he soon brought the conversation round to
sex and we all had a wank. We enjoyed ourselves and
agreed to return the next day. In fact we went back
several times, sometimes twice a day, and it wasn't
long before the man was fucking us both quite regularly. I could take him quite easily but my brother
was less relaxed and on just one occasion found it
very painful. After that he became increasingly
frightened about the visits and eventually refused to
come with me. I didn't like going on my own and that
was the end of that.

I grew up gay and still enjoy both fucking and
being fucked. My brother, on the other hand, is
happily married with two young children. His attitude towards child sex abuse is vitriolic. He says it
scarred him for life. I took it in my stride and have no
regrets.

Would you care to comment?

Hayden (North Wales)

It is virtually impossible to assess the degree of psychological
harm which a child either does or does not experience. In the
case of you and your brother who knows where the greatest
harm was done? You may not mind being gay — perhaps that
was your destiny anyway — but can we be sure your experience didn't direct you into homosexuality? If so, we must ask
the question 'Is that good or bad?' On the other hand, has your
brother experienced even greater emotional trauma?

There are so many imponderables that it is far too dangerous to try to justify or condone adults interfering with developing childhood sexuality. I may hold one view. Someone else may hold another. Who is to say who is right and who is wrong?

More On Child Abuse

Dear Ray,

I have never felt able to talk about my own experiences in order to protect my father who used to fuck me regularly from my very earliest memories right up until the time I left home when I was sixteen. By that time I was, of course, able to ejaculate and usually did so when we were together. Latterly I wanted to fuck him but he would never let me.

He died a few weeks ago and now I feel that I can speak out. At the time I don't think I resented what he was doing. We were always good friends and the fact that I used to cum myself suggests that I enjoyed what was going on. He had a big cock and there were times, especially in the early days, when it hurt, but he always tried to be gentle and I'm sure what he was doing was out of love and not simply lust.

The question arises, was I harmed by the experience? I'm now thirty-two and divorced. I married at nineteen, but the marriage only lasted two years. I was completely impotent with my wife. Then I had a couple of gay affairs without any sexual problems and married a second time at the age of twenty-seven. That marriage also folded about a year ago because, again, I was completely impotent with my wife. We are still good friends but she wanted a child so we mutually decided to part. I'm now back in another gay relationship and, once more, I have no sexual problems whatsoever. It may be significant that all my homosexual activities have been with substantially older men.

Reg (Portsmouth)

Once again it is very hard to be sure of the effect your father's behaviour had on you. Certainly the circumstantial evidence would support the idea that his activities were instrumental in setting the scene for your successful homosexual relationships and impotence with your wives, but it could be deeper than you think. After all, your two failed marriages were dramatically ended in the divorce court, but you are now also into at least your third homosexual relationship. You didn't need the legal formality of divorce for their break-up, but they occurred nevertheless. Perhaps they were less successful than would appear at first sight.

You say that you always got on well with your father and must have enjoyed his advances latterly because he made you cum. It could be that you were always inherently homosexual and that from the very earliest of your sexual experiences you were more than a willing participant. Young kids can twist their parents around their little fingers and, maybe without fully appreciating it, you actually seduced your father from the very beginning.

Try not to dwell on the past. Nothing can change it. Far better to come to terms with the lifestyle which is opening up before you. Learn to enjoy it and make the most of it because you only live once — as far as I know!

TV Turn-On

Dear Ray,

I'm turned on by TV... Not to watch it but just to have it blaring away in the background while my partner and I indulge in 'extra-curricular' activities. I suspect it is to do with the fact that, as a kid, I had to do my homework, eat dinner, try to communicate with the rest of the family and do everything in competition with the TV. It used to make me really angry.

Now I find that I don't watch it at all, but the anger is still there, converted into a sort of passion that works real wonders for my sex life.

It's quite hilarious really. My partner is fairly tolerant but sometimes stuffs his ears with cotton wool. Perhaps I should adjust to a quieter relationship.

K.D.K. (Brighton)

TV, to my mind, equates with transvestism and when I glanced at your opening sentence I thought that a topic on which I rarely get a letter was about to get an airing.

Your analysis of the situation is probably quite good: it sounds quite professional anyway. It isn't uncommon for guys to feel that their passions are aroused by high decibel pop music and the banging of native drums — that's why there is so much overt sexual display (gyrating and thrusting hips etc.) amongst pop stars.

Swinging The Lead

Dear Ray,

I love having my balls stretched during sex and like to wear a collar around the neck of my scrotum from which to suspend lead weights. I can cope fairly comfortably with a half-hundredweight. It's great to receive a blow job when I'm fully weighted down and my guy who does it for me tells me that I give him a hell of a lot more to swallow under such circumstances.

Incidentally, I have always had very low hanging balls and you may be interested to know that I continuously wear a thick leather collar four inches wide with complete comfort. It is from this collar that I suspend the weights. I am just awaiting completion of a five-inch cylindrical metal collar cushioned at the

top and bottom with sorbo rubber to prevent chafing.
I nearly went for a six-inch version but decided it was
a bit too tight. For fitting it opens lengthwise on two
hinges and, when in place, I keep it closed with a
couple of leather straps around it.

My guy thinks my low swingers are really great.
He keeps telling me that the only reason he's still
with me after three years is because he's so fascinated. I don't know whether that's a compliment or
not!

I have two questions: 1) What is the maximum safe
weight load I can carry without injury? 2) Why should
I produce more spunk when I've got the weights on?

John (London)

The mind boggles! I really don't know the answer to either of
your questions. Some people will be able to take greater loads
than others but stretching always carries with it the risk of
injury, especially the development of varicose veins (varic-
ocele) in the vessels from the testicles and perhaps a hydro-
cele which is an accumulation of fluid in the scrotal sac. If you
are determined to go to such lengths then the responsibility
must rest entirely with you.

One of my very earliest memories from when I was perhaps five years old was of visiting the Bertram Mills circus
and seeing the giraffe-necked women from Africa (or somewhere) who had stretched their necks incredibly by adding
one metal ring on top of another over many years. If they can
do it with their necks I don't suppose there is any physical
reason why soft tissues like the scrotal neck shouldn't be
elongated. But rather you than me.

Maybe you produce more spunk when you are weighted
down because of your higher state of arousal.

I've heard of cloying boyfriends being described as 'coming
on heavy', but this puts a new slant on it.

Putting His Foot In It

Dear Ray,

I have lived with my present partner for three and a half years. He's the dominant type but it isn't exactly a master/slave relationship. A while ago we tried fist-fucking. I couldn't take very much at first but, over several months and with the aid of poppers, we managed it — a whole fist. Eventually it became quite easy and he plunges in one fist after the other, in and out in quick succession. I love it and he couldn't get enough either.

Recently he had the idea of foot-fucking. I coped well with the toes and ball of the foot but I couldn't get the heel in, so he stopped when I asked. Then one night we played around with bondage and I got tied to the bed in a very uncomfortable position. After a bit of fisting he tried his foot again. I couldn't use poppers and, being tied up, I couldn't wriggle free. Although it was very painful he wouldn't stop even though I cried out. Then, with a final kick, the rest of his foot went right in. I bled quite a lot and afterwards I was in a lot of pain. I haven't had sex with him for three weeks, even though he has apologised. I know he is now seeing other men.

Three and a half years is a long time to throw away. Should I trust him again, or should I tell him to pack his bags?

Ted (Ashton-Under-Lyme)

I try to be tolerant of many things but your partner could have killed you... And I mean it. Never allow yourself to be tied up and exposed to that threat again, and don't rely on poppers to ease the pain. Your gut could have been ruptured and you may not have realised the damage until it was too late. Fisting/footing is really very risky. At the very least you are likely to damage the anal sphincter muscles which could lead eventually to faecal incontinence, and you are bound to suffer cuts and abrasions through which infection can easily enter.

As to the future of your relationship, if I were in your shoes I'd pull my finger out as quickly as I could, before he puts his foot in it again!

●●●

It is letters like the above which bring the whole of gay sex into disrepute. No wonder the ordinary straight man in the street is revolted. Yes, I know that similar excesses occur at the fringes of heterosexual behaviour, but the unfortunate added stigma of gayness makes us so terribly vulnerable. It is all rather nicely summed up in the final letter of this chapter....

The Gay Sex Image

Dear Ray,

One of the problems which bedevils straight society's ability to see gayness as a totally acceptable alternative sexual outlet is aesthetic revulsion at some of the things we do during love-making.

A very dear and long-standing straight friend of mine knew me to be gay and appeared quite indifferent to the fact until, during a recent intimate chat, he asked me what I did in bed with my lover. When I explained, as tactfully as I could with carefully chosen words, that I sucked his cock, swallowed his semen and actually enjoyed the flavour, I could see the look of utter horror cross my friend's face. It was too late to draw back. He expressed his disgust, left and has refused even to acknowledge me since, except to look at me with undisguised revulsion in his eyes. It is just as well that I never had the chance to go any further into my arse-rimming, water sports, and other activities.

In the context of 'love' all this sort of behaviour, and more, assumes a naturalness and beauty which quite belies its 'yukky' superficial image yet I now feel guilty and ashamed. Somehow the lovely spontaneity has gone out of my relationship with my boyfriend. My problem is now one of guilt and depression, which is why I've turned to you for help.

Robert (Cardiff)

I suggest that your shocked friend is either very naïve about what goes on even in the most apparently respectable heterosexual relationships or else he has a deep guilt problem of his own which has surfaced as a result of your confession.

I have no doubt that many heterosexual marriages never proceed further than somewhat formalised sexual intercourse in the 'male superior missionary position', and many homosexual affairs are equally unadventurous. However, we live in an exciting world of widespread hetero- and homosexual experimentation to discover ways of enhancing the joys of sexual contact. As I said at the beginning of this chapter the borders of what used to be called 'perversion' are being steadily pushed further and further back.

Nowadays, all you describe as being features of homosexual behaviour are equally part of many a happy heterosexual couple's repertoire. We may carry the added stigma of being gay but you've nothing to feel guilty or ashamed about. Your friend is simply behind the times.

7

THE FROLIC AND THE FOLLY

When 'consenting adults' were legally allowed out of the closet to relax and join in with the swinging sixties little did they realise that a big bad bear was waiting around the corner.

Its first growls were heard from faraway San Francisco. There in 1981, a few gay men died from a strange combination of symptoms which suggested that their body defences were failing to protect them against a number of very rare infections.

Gradually, as the numbers grew, and Terrence Higgins was amongst the first to die here in Great Britain, the world awoke to the realisation that a new sexually transmitted disease, a killer, was amongst us. We have now come to know it as Acquired Immune Deficiency Syndrome (AIDS) caused by the Human Immunodeficiency Virus (HIV). As I write, in February 1991, about four people every day are dying from AIDS in the UK alone and the total of deaths worldwide, since the beginning of the epidemic, runs into hundreds of thousands.

It is hard to be on the gay scene nowadays and not know someone whose life has been touched, either directly or indirectly, by HIV, and the fear of infection has certainly dampened enthusiasm for the new-found sexual freedoms we were beginning to enjoy. I had one very special friend, Chris (the only name I haven't changed throughout this book), who died at Easter in 1990 when he was only twenty-five. I think of him a lot and it is to him that I dedicate this chapter. How often have I thought 'if only' and reminded myself yet once again of the rules of safer sex. Vaccines or cures may eventually be developed but, until they are, there is nothing more important than to mean it when we so often use that rather glib expression, 'take care'!

I am not going to fall into the trap of writing a long text book about HIV and AIDS. There are many other sources of information, but I receive a regular stream of letters on the subject and I must devote some pages to it.

At the same time I must mention a few of the other 'nasties' which occasionally rear their ugly heads in my HIM column.

The Frolic And The Folly

Dear Ray,

I am a young man who is extremely frightened after having anal intercourse.

I came out to my close family on New Year's Eve and they accepted the situation very well. The next evening I went to a local gay pub for just the second time ever. I was hoping to meet some gay friends of my own age who I had met there a few days earlier but they didn't turn up. I was nervous, being alone, and got very drunk. I was picked up by a twenty-eight year old who said that he had been sexually active since the age of nine and I went back to his place to have sex. He kept assuring me that he wouldn't do anything that I didn't want to but one thing led to another and, before I knew it, he had fucked me without using a condom. Everything seemed to happen so quickly that I never had time to think about what we were doing. It is true that an erect cock listens to no one. He was the first person I had ever had sex with and in the morning he told me that I was so drunk that I couldn't even cum.

As I write I feel degraded, used, cheap and physically sick with fear. I also feel angry that someone has gained a quick thrill through my inexperience. I know all about safer sex and feel so guilty for not having carried it out. I've let myself down, and my family who were so understanding when I came out. I know it takes up to six months before an HIV antibody test will prove positive. In the meantime I feel isolated and I can't talk to anyone.

Perhaps this letter can be used as a warning to others — especially inexperienced people like myself.

Anthony (Deal)

There is no way that I can give you an absolute guarantee that you haven't been infected and the trouble is that once you've acquired HIV you have no second chances.

However, let's not get things out of perspective. Thousands upon thousands of fuckings go on every day of the year and still only a very small percentage of the population is infected. One can play with statistics in all sorts of ways both to frighten and to reassure. In your case, being realistic, the actual chances of having been infected from your one-off indiscretion are pretty remote so keep your pecker up and if all is well let's hope that you (and others who read your letter) will be warned of the folly of the indiscriminate frolic.

I don't blame you for what has happened. You are young and virile and it is so easy to be carried away by enthusiasm, especially when you have a few drinks inside you. You were under stress, having just come out to your family, but you mustn't reproach yourself too severely. You can't go through life feeling degraded, cheap and used every time you have some sexual fun... But you can go through life being careful.

The Risk Factor

Dear Ray,

Clearly not everyone who's fucked by an HIV-positive individual automatically becomes infected first time around. If so the prevalence of HIV infection in society would be far greater than it apparently is.

Just how risky are the various sexual activities as far as AIDS is concerned?

Andrew (Birmingham)

Surprisingly enough, Human Immunodeficiency Virus, which gives rise to AIDS, is not a particularly infectious agent. The chances of not being infected when one is in contact with a possible source of infection far outweigh the chances of being caught. However, that's not much consolation to the unlucky guy whose number is on the ticket!

In the world population as a whole best estimates are that only about one in a hundred, or even as low as one in a thousand, incidents of sexual intercourse with an infected person lead to the virus being transmitted. Even so, 75 per cent of all known cases of AIDS have been sexually acquired. Worldwide, AIDS is far more common amongst heterosexuals than it is amongst gays. The 75 per cent above consists of 60 per cent vaginally transmitted and only 15 per cent anally transmitted cases. In gay sex the risk to the passive (receptive) partner in anal intercourse is probably a hundredfold greater than the risk to the active partner.

Sadly, it is statistics of this kind which lead guys to become complacent and give up safer sex precautions. What we forget is that there are quite a few million incidents of sexual intercourse in Britain every day and that's why the numbers of infected people keep on going up and up.

Probably the risk from sharing needles amongst intravenous drug users is also about one in a hundred. Drug users make up about 7 per cent of the total number of cases up to the present time but their share of the total is rapidly increasing.

Although only 5 per cent of the world's cases have been due to infected blood transfusions probably more than 90 per cent of those transfused with infected blood will develop AIDS. 10 per cent of the total cases are children born to infected mothers with the risk to any individual baby in these circumstances being about 30 per cent. In hospitals about 1 in 200 care workers accidentally pricked by an infected needle may become infected, but they make up less than 0.1 per cent of the total number of cases.

Possibly the greatest danger is complacency. Not so long ago AIDS was on everybody's lips and a new world order of sexually responsible behaviour seemed to be emerging. But old habits die hard. Standards are slipping again. Gonorrhoea, one of the earliest markers of unprotected sexual activity, is once again on the increase. The risk factors could be about to change.

●●●

Condoms are a must if you intend to practise anal sex, though it has to be said that they are only a damage limitation exercise. It is a fact that fucking is so much a part of so many gay men's sexual repertoires that it isn't really practical to expect everyone to give it up in favour of safer activities, though that would be the ideal solution. So I can't emphasise enough the need to use a condom every time unless you are 100 per cent sure that your partner is not now, nor has been in the last ten years, getting himself screwed by anyone else.

Quite a few letters raise issues about condoms...

The All-Enveloping Sheath

Dear Ray,
        The mail order advert promised added protection against infection by the use of this special all-enveloping sheath which incorporated a balls bag as well as the usual cock sock.
        It seemed a good idea and I bought one, but the practical problem of putting it on defeats me entirely. Because of the bag end it can't be rolled on in the same way as an ordinary sheath and has to be pulled

on like a glove. That's not very easy with a fairly big
tool, though the actual tube is a comfortably snug fit
when I eventually do manage it. But then there is the
even bigger difficulty of getting the bag over my balls.
I can usually get one in then, when I stretch the
opening to manipulate the other, the first one pops
out again. There is a slightly thicker rubber ring at
the opening but it certainly isn't strong enough to
hold down a pair of bollocks which seem determined
to escape upwards into the sanctity of my groin as
orgasm approaches.

What am I supposed to do?

Ryan (Dewsbury)

Not knowing the answer I was tempted to buy one myself in
order to experiment. It seems we both have a useless bit of
rubber on our hands — certainly not on our pricks!

After a helluva lot of struggling I did manage to get the
damn thing on but being faced with that problem while on a
high plateau of arousal in the arms of a lover is enough to put
anyone off. It seemed to me to be a sure way to encourage the
intended wearer to chuck it away in disgust and risk bareback action instead. That could be very foolish.

These all-enveloping sheaths are washable and intended
for re-use. They're pretty thick but that doesn't mean to say
that they are any safer than the more traditional thin latex
varieties. The thicker rubber may be less readily stretched
and could, therefore, split more easily in use. What's more it
becomes even more important that one uses a water-soluble
lubricant (eg. KY) because the corrosive effect of other lubricants on the rubber could prove cumulative on a re-usable
sheath.

Whether or not ordinary washable contraceptive sheaths
are still on the market I'm afraid I haven't been able to
discover. They were available until a few years ago but were
very thick and unpopular because of the loss of sensation
which was involved.

Some guys are sensitive to the latex from which condoms are made. Animal gut condoms are available and the commonest brand name in the UK is 'Four X'. I do not know about their efficiency as a barrier to HIV. It is also possible to purchase the so-called 'American Tips' — little round 'balloons' which simply cover the glans penis. Though better than nothing they may slip off rather easily.

Rubber Dangers

Dear Ray,
   Warning: if you buy any condoms out of a vending machine watch out that they don't split when putting them on your own or your boyfriend's prick. I've found this happens during our 'nookie' sessions... on the rare occasions when I get it!

Ken (Heathrow)

Dear Ray,
   I recently had rubbers burst on me on two separate occasions. I have always had difficulty in putting lubricated rubbers on, perhaps because my dick (just over seven inches long and six inches round the thickest part) is bigger than most I've seen.

Martin (Edinburgh)

These are both very short and substantially edited extracts from two long letters. They highlight the very serious issue of condom reliability in the present AIDS crisis and, indeed, some of the London clinics report that most of their gay clients now blame condom breakage as the cause of their infection.

First it has to be emphasised that the British Kitemark Standard for condom manufacture, even though it has been upgraded recently, is still very strictly related to suitability for vaginal, not anal, use. There is no reason to believe that vending machine condoms are any different from those sold over the counter but, at either point of sale, the product, especially if manufactured abroad, may not match even the Kitemark standard. There is no requirement that all condoms must do so.

Ken's reference to the occasional nature of his 'nookie' sessions draws attention to the need for practice and familiarity with condom use. Clumsy, inexperienced application can easily lead to splitting, perhaps by finger nails or even teeth if the package is difficult to tear open.

I have referred elsewhere in this book to the increasing availability of different sized condoms for beyond average users. Condoms are either plain-ended or else they have a small teat reservoir at the end to collect the semen. They may, or may not, be lubricated. Individual users will have their own personal preferences. It has been suggested that the plain-ended, non-lubricated type are better for anal use because they tear less frequently at the tip and, being dry inside, are less likely to slip off. A water-soluble external lubricant can be applied for ease of penetration.

Nonoxinol 9

Dear Ray,

I like being fucked and I like to suck and I'm available to several partners each week. Fortunately I'm HIV-negative and I intend to be careful to ensure I stay that way. I always use a condom for both anal and oral sex.

I used to use dry condoms, lubricated on the outside only with KY, for arse work, but when I heard that lubricants containing Nonoxinol 9 spermicide were lethal to HIV I went over to ready-lubed johnnies for added protection. I now find that my arse becomes sore and inflamed and, at the same time, rather numb so that sensation is lost. Similarly my tongue gets a bit sore and my mouth feels a bit dead.

Is this a common problem?

Harry (Scunthorpe)

There is growing evidence that a few people are sensitive to Nonoxinol 9 and react in the way you describe. A recent study in Edinburgh amongst rent boys and 'working girls' showed that quite a high percentage preferred to be ridden bareback than use the Nonoxinol 9-lubricated condoms which were being distributed free.

As a sore bum with inflamed tissues is potentially more dangerous as far as becoming infected is concerned I suggest that you revert to using dry condoms and KY. If you want to carry on buying lubricated condoms check on the package to see whether the lubricant contains the spermicide.

Imperfect Packaging

Dear Roy,

My mate tells me that he prefers to use a tight, all-enveloping, application of Cling Film wrapping to a standard condom. He says it is equally sensitive and tight fitting and, with a bit of judicious binding, he can enclose, and thus protect, his balls as well.

It strikes me that he's got it all wrapped up — do you agree?

Neville (Guernsey)

The amazing thing about this barmy idea is that you aren't the first to write to me about it. I must have had three or four letters with variations on the theme and I'm just waiting for the first guy to come up with the suggestion that we use aluminium cooking foil.

It isn't as if condoms are really expensive to buy and surely the days of embarrassment while purchasing them are long since past. I can't think why any twit should want to risk such imperfect packaging.

Mind you, I once saw a gay stripper whose final layer of cover was a length of Cling Film wound around him like a loin cloth. Very erotic it looked too!

Is Sucking Safer?

Dear Ray,

I read that you advocate that sucking is safer. I am concerned about whether you limit this simply to the 'Big A' or can any of the more common venereal infections be picked up by either sucking or being sucked? In other words are the more common and less dangerous venereal diseases contracted only by anal/ vaginal intercourse and not by sucking. I have been sucked several times and have wondered whether I could contract any disease from the saliva of my partner.

Jamie (Leicester)

You are right to raise this issue. Nowadays we all tend to be so obsessed by HIV/AIDS that we forget all the other diseases that can be sexually transmitted.

Unfortunately other diseases can be spread though cock-sucking and rimming.

Where an open sore is involved as, for example, in herpes or primary syphilis in or around the mouth of the guy who is doing the sucking, then the guy being sucked may well become infected. Similarly, when the sore is on the cock or balls of the guy who is being sucked his sucker is at risk. However, the guy who is doing the sucking is the one who is more likely to be the one who gets infected with diseases like hepatitis B and HIV (where the virus is in the semen), or gonorrhoea, or non-specific urethritis or NSU (where the infecting bacteria can cause a penile discharge). The saliva of an infected person very rarely causes any problems to the guy who is being sucked.

Rimming is a risky game for the rimmer. All sorts of 'nasties' from the intestinal tract can be picked up in this way, even, some say, Kaposi's sarcoma, which is one of the main complications of people who are infected with HIV. Luckily for the guy who is being rimmed, however, he has a fairly safe time of it unless, again, the rimmer has open sores on his mouth or tongue.

Sucking is believed to be safer as far as HIV is concerned because the theoretical risk to a sucker who gets a mouthful of spunk never seems to have materialised in practice. In the one or two cases where this is thought to have been the possible route of infection the confirmatory evidence is subject to quite a lot of criticism. If there is a risk it must be very remote indeed, and even more remote for the guy who is having his cock gobbled on. I think, however, that anyone would be tempting fate just a little too complacently if he were to 'suck and be damned' with someone he knew to be HIV-positive.

AIDS Illogicalities

Dear Ray,

Three years ago I lived in cloud-cuckoo land. I read all sorts of horror stories about how AIDS was invariably fatal within a year or two; there was no cure, no vaccine and the slow lingering death was the most terrifying and cataclysmic experience known to man.

Frightened out of my wits I thought that I was being careful and that no harm would befall me, Then the bomb dropped — I was found to be HIV-positive. I think I know the one sad occasion when, where and how it happened, but that's now water under the bridge. Fortunately I'm still in good health but I'm intrigued at the way the experts have changed their tune. I'm told not to despair and that, maybe, I'll not succumb to the fullblown AIDS and that there's so much I can do to improve my chances of leading a long and symptom-free life.

Naturally in my present condition I'm all for this constant reassurance and encouragement, but I can't help feeling that two standards are being adopted and my confidence is being undermined by all the black horror stories used to encourage safer sex amongst the fortunate non-infected.

Richard (Cleveland)

On the face of it there does appear to be a conflict of interests here. We've got to impress upon the non-infected that HIV infection can't be ignored and precautions are a life-saving essential, but at the same time we must boost and maintain the morale of those, like yourself, who have acquired the infection.

Because most infected people eventually progress to the full AIDS syndrome and because there is, as yet, no cure or vaccine, we have to adopt a somewhat fatalistic approach and use these facts to impress upon sexually active guys the need to take care — even if this is at the expense of the sensitivities of those who are infected.

On the other hand, the situation for those who are HIV-positive is better than it was and improving every day. We are becoming much more confident in our use of AZT and other drugs which are in the pipeline and which influence the behaviour of the causative virus itself. We are also developing improved skills at treating the various infections and other problems which arise as secondary consequences of the infection. As time goes by the glimmer of light at the end of the tunnel is getting slowly, but progressively, brighter and it would be quite wrong to ignore this fact.

My Lover Has AIDS

Dear Ray,

I have just discovered what is probably the most horrible thing that has ever happened to me. My partner has AIDS. I became defensive against other people's reactions rather than offensive against my partner. I have always been protective of him, but now it has become obsessional.

I still get in a muddle between HIV and AIDS. We have always been very careful — safe sex and all that — so I never expected it. I was tested and am OK at present, though I've got to go back for retests in a few months time. I have to keep telling him to stop saying 'sorry'. It must have been some other bastard in his past with a sadistic approach to sex who is to blame. My partner is my life and I won't ever forget that.

I wish the media would get wise to the fact that AIDS is still with us. I heard a bloke say, 'Don't hear much about it now — it's probably not happening now.' I might even start to cry the next time I hear someone say that but my partner jokes, 'Save your tears for after the party — after the death of the walking dead.' I hate that. My only puzzle is what happens now?

Anon. (Edinburgh)

Why should you be surprised at your reaction? You say your partner is your life. If he means so much to you then, of course, you will wish to protect him against those who are offensive. At times of adversity love should bring people closer together, not drive them apart.

But do not condemn as a 'bastard' some former partner who was responsible for your lover's infection. The chances are that he was totally unaware of his own infection and would be extremely distressed to learn that he had passed it on. For all you know he, too, may now be dead or dying and feeling just as irrationally bitter and frustrated about the source of his own infection.

So far the gay community has borne the brunt of the HIV/AIDS epidemic in the western world. The predominant qualities have been bravery, stoicism, incredible mutual support and loving responsibility and pride. HIV has brought out the best in our ranks — the bastards have been few.

If your lover is merely HIV antibody-positive he may enjoy a normal lifespan of good health. The evidence is that the period of time from the date of infection to the development of symptomatic AIDS averages as long as eight to ten years and it still remains possible that for many infected persons the time could be much longer.

What happens next depends upon how far your lover's infection has progressed, the extent to which he looks after himself and leads a healthy lifestyle, and the counselling and therapy which he receives from the services available in your area. Your own continued caring support is paramount and, provided you continue to play safe there's no reason why you shouldn't go on enjoying a fulfilling love life together. That's something you will both need to sustain you in the testing times ahead.

One important matter for the future which will have to be tackled, no matter how distasteful, is sorting out both your wills. Because gay couples are not protected by the contract of marriage enjoyed by heterosexual couples serious difficulties can arise if one or other partner dies intestate. You cannot automatically expect his belongings to come your way. You have no right of possession, for example, if you have a shared house mortgage, or even a hire purchase agreement on a car or hi-fi. Other members of his family would come first and you could lose out disastrously if there isn't a proper will.

●●●

You can be sure that AIDS will continue to cause all sorts of issues to be raised for a very long time to come. Culling past pages of HIM brings out matters of confidentiality, housing, employment, insurance, treatment and care, safer sex, etc., etc. but I can't go on for ever so here's a slight change of subject... hepatitis B.

Hepatitis B — Carrier State

Dear Ray,
Recently I had the HIV antibody test and was relieved to learn that I was negative. However, at the same time, my blood was tested for hepatitis B antibodies and I was told that this test was positive.

In a way I'm not surprised because I know this infection is more easily spread than HIV and usually by the same sexual practices. I'm no virgin!

However, I have no recollection of ever having been ill and I am now worried as to whether or not I am still infectious because I'm told that hepatitis B carriers can feel quite well in themselves but can pass on the disease for the rest of their lives.

Can you tell me a bit more please?

'Olly' (Crewe)

As you say, the hepatitis B virus spreads sexually in the same way as Human Immunodeficiency Virus which is the cause of AIDS. Hepatitis B can be a very serious disease leading to liver destruction and death in some cases. Those who survive often experience debilitating symptoms which continue for many months.

However, not all those who are infected fall ill. Sometimes they suffer no symptoms whatsoever and simply develop protective antibodies in their blood which give them an immunity to subsequent attack by the virus. Still others who become infected, whilst they may recover from their acute illness, or even not show any symptoms at all, are unable to get rid of live virus particles from their blood stream. These people, up to 10 per cent of the total numbers infected, can become infectious carriers and may remain so for anything from a few months to the rest of their natural lives. Blood tests are available which show whether a person merely possesses antibodies which confer a state of immunity upon him, or whether he is still a carrier of live infectious virus particles.

The virus has a much higher infectivity than HIV which means that it is more readily transmitted from one person to another and, for example, can be spread quite readily by cock sucking or rimming whereas the risk of HIV spreading in these ways is very low indeed. This means that an apparently healthy carrier can be a serious menace if he is leading an active sex life with a large number of partners.

Whilst I cannot be sure, and therefore I recommend that you seek further local information and testing if necessary, I imagine that once you were discovered to be hepatitis B antibody-positive — which means that you are now fortunately immune to further attack by the virus — a further test would have been undertaken to discover whether you were also a carrier. My guess is that this test probably proved negative otherwise you would have been told of your hazard status as far as others are concerned.

The really good news about hep. B is that an effective vaccine is available and all gay people are officially encouraged to go along to their GP or, if they would prefer it, their local STD clinic to receive the course of three monthly injections. The ordinary prescription fee will apply through the GP but the service is free in the clinic.

●●●

Hepatitis B can interfere with relationships in unexpected ways...

A Question Of Fidelity

Dear Ray,

Since I met my current lover two years ago I have been totally loyal to him. Recently he went down with hepatitis B. Fortunately it was a relatively mild attack and he has made a complete recovery. He swears that he, too, has been equally faithful to me and insists that he must have caught it from me and that, therefore, I must have been sleeping around. As you can imagine, this is posing a serious threat to our relationship.

I'm not aware of ever having had hepatitis B and I haven't been tested for antibodies, but even if I were to be found positive I don't see that it would prove anything. Perhaps I could have been infected by him. Maybe he is the one who has been doing the 'two-timing', though I'm trying to give him the benefit of the doubt.

Ray (St Helens)

Living a life of mutual suspicion with your lover is no good for anyone, but the trouble is that neither one of you is ever likely to know for sure where the infection came from. It is important though to remember that, because it is quite highly infectious, it isn't only spread by sexual activity. It is possible that either one of you might have been accidentally infected by an infected needle, or you could have been infected in some other way. Has either one of you been getting any tattoos, for example?

Your lover's recent illness points to his having become infected within the past two or three months, but that doesn't exclude you from having been a long-term unsuspecting carrier. I agree that if you were to test positive it would tell you nothing about whether you were infected before or after his illness, but a negative result, should it prove to be so, would confirm that your lover must have acquired his infection elsewhere. Only you can decide whether you want to explore that possibility.

●●●

I receive surprisingly few letters about the 'traditional' venereal diseases. I guess the symptoms are so evident that infected guys go to the clinic straight away, cutting out the middle man.

Clapped Out

> Dear Ray,
> Three days ago I fucked a stranger. Yesterday I had a terrible burning sensation in my prick whenever I went for a piss and today I've got a whiteish discharge oozing from the tip. I'm terrified I might have caught AIDS. What should I do?
>
> Tony (London)

Fortunately you were sensible enough to send me a stamped addressed envelope and I was able to reply advising you to attend your local STD clinic straight away.

Nowadays we are all so hyped up about AIDS, hepatitis B and herpes that a lot of people are forgetting that the traditional venereal diseases haven't gone away. You describe the typical train of events associated with gonorrhoea or, possibly, NSU. Early treatment of such conditions is usually 100 per cent effective and you should never hesitate to go along to a clinic. Treatment is confidential and non-judgemental. No one is going to get uptight because you are gay.

It will be three months or even longer before you can be sure that you haven't acquired HIV/AIDS. It takes that long for a blood test to show up positive after the date of infection.

You'll just have to wait patiently with your fingers crossed. However, take heart from the fact that it is very rare indeed for the active partner to be infected during anal intercourse. It is the passive partner who is at greatest risk.

Classic Syphilis

Dear Ray,

About twelve years ago when I developed a skin rash, the clinic doctor diagnosed classic syphilis, showed me to his medical students and asked me if I'd mind being photographed — perhaps you've seen me in the text books! After eight weeks of daily injections and a sore bum I was pronounced cured.

What bothers me is that, at the time, I had had only two recent sexual experiences. The first was about six months previously when, after a boozy party, I slept with a guy who raped me. When I spoke to him about it he denied any responsibility and said that the only treatment he had had recently was for a stomach ulcer. The second was a guy I sucked who didn't even cum in my mouth.

A rather spotty heterosexual youth stayed with me about that time and may have shared my bathroom towel inadvertently. Could he have been the cause?

Is there any truth in several articles I've read in the gay press linking syphilis with HIV infection?

David (Solihull)

There are three 'classic' stages of syphilis. The first, which is often missed, is the primary stage when a small sore or 'chancre' appears at the site of entry of the infection — usually the penis, anus or lip. This may be quite small, totally painless and dismissed as an unimportant pimple. It usually disappears after a week or two.

The secondary stage appears about six months later and is typified by a widespread body rash and general feeling of malaise. This was the stage you were at when your doctor wanted to photograph you. The timing is just about right for you to have been infected by the guy who raped you. Sometimes even this stage passes unnoticed and it is quite likely that your partner genuinely thought he was not to blame.

The third, and most serious stage, may occur years later, after the infection has lain hidden and dormant in some part of your body for a very long time. It can emerge in all sorts of frightening ways from madness to blindness. In fact, third stage (tertiary) syphilis can mimic almost any other disease. Fortunately your timely treatment spared you that problem.

The only reason that HIV infection is linked with syphilis is that both are spread sexually and so it is on the cards for someone who has been infected by one to have been infected by the other at the same time.

●●●

I have already warned that rimming even an apparently clean arse carries risks. Quite a number of infections and infestations pass from person to person this way. Here's one example with which to round off this chapter.

Worm's Eye View

Dear Ray,

Please can you help me with a rather embarrassing problem. I like rimming my boyfriend and I think — I know — I've picked up threadworms. I've got an itchy backside which sometimes delivers a few little white worms. I looked up several medical books, but they didn't say what to do about it.

Can you tell me if there is a human equivalent of what dogs get slipped into their Kennomeat? And can you get it by mail order? One of the books suggested a garlic clove up the bum, but it doesn't work.

Roger (Coventry)

Threadworms (enterobius vermicularis) are nasty little buggers which aren't all that easily eradicated by the usual deworming pills. The females live in your rectum, wriggle out, usually while you are warm in bed at night, burrow into the skin around your arse and lay their eggs. That's what causes the itching and when you scratch you get the eggs under your finger nails and on your skin. Without realising it you transfer the eggs back into your mouth next time you eat food or put your hand to your lips. And so the cycle goes round and round. You almost certainly were infested in the first place by rimming your partner. Be careful, as it is very easy to pass on the infestation to other members of the family.

Any dispensing pharmacist will sell you 'Antepar' tablets without prescription and you should carefully follow the full instructions which will accompany them. It is usually necessary for everyone in the household to be treated simultaneously... and that includes your boyfriend and everyone he lives with.

But 'Antepar' is only part of the battle. Strict hygiene is probably even more important in order to break the cycle of re-infestation. You need to wash very thoroughly after wiping your bum and scrub under your fingernails. Keep a separate towel for everyone and, preferably, even a separate towel for your face. Try to keep your fingers away from your mouth at all times and wash thoroughly before meals. Don't eat with your fingers between meals. Think carefully and precautions will emerge as commonsense.

●●●

All I have tried to show in this chapter is that the joys of gay sex can be marred by a few nasties here and there. I certainly don't expect readers to turn to these pages as a reference point when they want to know what to do about everything from venereal warts to crab lice, scabies or herpes. Usually problems of this sort cannot be sorted out through an agony column and it is far more sensible to seek help straight away from your local GP or STD clinic.

8

WOE BETIDE US!

Ah, woe and misery me! Now we come to the real meat of my HIM Agony Uncle feature. In this chapter I shall try to answer just some of the hundreds of letters which ask questions specifically about *What's Wrong With My Willy?* — and balls, and all the other dangly bits which go to make up man's sexual armament.

Many A Time And Ouch!

Dear Ray,

I hate to admit it in a magazine so full of tales of rampant studs who spray their spunk around the place as if it flowed from a bottomless reservoir, but I normally cum only a couple of times a week.

However, on two recent occasions I've spent the night in bed with a lively guy who has managed to bring me off twice (during the first night) and three times (during the second night). It was tremendous at the time, especially number three on night two, but next day the ache in my balls and the lower part of my tummy was agony for about twenty-four hours. My cock, not surprisingly, was rubbed red and very sore. I expected the latter and wasn't worried about it but the ache did disturb me until it eased up.

Is there any risk of doing myself a permanent injury on such occasions?

Nigel (Poole)

The exploits of magazine studs often have to be taken with a pinch of salt and allowances made for author's licence. Millions of guys would think themselves very lucky to cum twice a week — and I mean millions, though, of course, there are also millions of others who shoot more often.

When you do any heavy exercise or activity that you aren't accustomed to you'll find that the muscles and tissues involved ache the following day. Those involved in violent outbursts of sexual action are no exception and may be even more vulnerable when you think of the pummelling your balls get from the wanking hand during vigorous masturbation. Don't worry, though, no permanent damage is likely to be caused by frequent orgasms.

You are quite right, second and subsequent orgasms following on shortly after a first are very often of much greater intensity, even though they may produce less spunk.

No Bloody Fear

Dear Ray,

I had a hell of a fright a couple of nights ago. My lover and I hadn't seen each other for about three weeks while he was working out of town. We were both feeling really hot for each other and went at it hammer and tongs all night. I can't remember how many times I came, but it was a lot. We forced ourselves time and again to make up for lost time.

Then it happened. I had an orgasm which was accompanied by an ejaculation of what looked like almost pure blood. It frightened the life out of me and it killed our passion stone dead.

I couldn't pluck up the courage to see my GP and have been sweating on it for almost forty-eight hours. Ten minutes ago I had a very gentle wank and my spunk seemed to be quite clear and normal again. But I'm still anxious. What should I do? Do you think I've harmed myself permanently?

Max (London)

Relax: a one-off squirt of blood after a period of intense and repeated sexual arousal is almost certainly nothing to worry about. It follows the tremendous engorgement of the various tubules and blood vessels which all the excitement produces in your reproductive tract. Some little blood capillary has 'popped' somewhere inside and it is quite probable that you did, in fact, ejaculate almost pure blood as a result. After so many enforced orgasms in such a short space of time there probably wasn't any ordinary spunk left in your system.

Chronic haemospermia — regular staining of your spunk with blood caused in the same way — can be quite common and some guys experience it every time they cum. Very occasionally there may be a true pathological cause — perhaps a little inflammation or a polyp or even an early cancerous growth — so, when the problem persists for a few weeks it is as well to visit a doctor for a check up. Usually it is quite harmless, but in someone who is HIV-positive the infectivity of their semen could be increased.

Understandably, it can be a bit off-putting to a partner, but I'm afraid there isn't much that can be done about it. When it is very bad and persistent a cystoscopic investigation under anaesthesia (passing a sort of telescope along the length of the penis) may enable a surgeon to spot the bleeding point and cauterise it electrically.

Cumming Thick

Dear Ray,

When I cum I don't shoot my load. It sort of comes out in a thick blob. Maybe this doesn't sound anything serious but, to me, it's awful. I won't let anyone see me cum and when I'm going with anyone I'm on pins. It's totally ruining my sex life. Am I alone in this?

Jim (Sheffield)

Indeed you are certainly not alone. Some guys have very watery spunk and tend to ejaculate quite a large volume. Others produce much less which is often thick and gooey, almost like jelly on occasions.

The spermatozoa coming from your testicles are in jelly form. The semen only becomes liquid upon the addition of the fluid from the prostate gland and the seminal vesicles (both at the neck of the bladder where the tubes from the testicles join the urethra). The liquidity of your cum depends entirely upon the amount of fluid added, and that varies from person to person and, indeed, sometimes even in the same person from day to day and depending upon the frequency of his orgasms.

The power to shoot your spunk depends on three factors: 1) the fluidity (viscosity) of your semen; 2) the diameter and length of your urethra; and 3) the force with which the muscles contract at orgasm in order to squirt it out. Since you have very thick spunk it isn't surprising that you don't shoot it very far,

But, cheer up, what you have is probably of very good quality and highly concentrated. I do think you are going a bit over the top in suggesting that your sex life is being ruined. I'm just a little concerned that you are sheltering behind your clotted cream as an excuse to explain away a deeper and more significant reason for your being on pins when you should be relaxed and enjoying your sexual relationships with a partner.

Quick As A Flash

Dear Ray,

I see my lover about once a week and look forward to getting together with him with ever-growing excitement as each meeting gets nearer. Recently, however, I've had a couple of disasters. I've been so worked up that as soon as we've got undressed I've cum before we've even got into bed.

I've always been a bit quick on the trigger, but now it's becoming impossible. By the way, I'm twenty-two if that has any relevance.

Tony (Bracknell)

Another Quick Dick!

Dear Ray,

I have not been on the gay scene for very long but I have managed to develop a relationship with a loving and warm person who is very sexually experienced.

However, I do have a problem. I feel that my penis is much more sensitive than it should be. For example, during oral sex I can only hold out for a fraction of the time that my partner can. I come off far too quickly and I'm afraid it is beginning to affect our relationship.

Exactly the same happens during anal sex. The sensation is far too strong for me to continue for any length of time and this is causing my partner increasing frustration. Just as soon as I get inside him I cum and I don't know how to make it last longer.

It wouldn't matter so much if I could carry on after I've cum but all I want to do then is lie back and rest leaving him to bring himself off by solo masturbation.

Anon. (Powys)

Fast Food

Dear Ray,

Ever since my balls dropped at the age of thirteen I've been a regular wanker and looking forward to being sucked off for the first time. That was always my fantasy of the ultimate sexual delight.

Well, at last it happened four or five nights ago. I'm twenty-three now so you can imagine my excitement at the prospect of my first date after a decade of waiting. I could really feel my heart bumping and I was shivering like a jelly even though I wasn't cold.

We stripped off and lay on the bed. He went down on me straight away and, disaster of disasters, I shot my load and gave him a mouthful almost before he'd tightened his lips around my knob. We did it again last night and exactly the same thing happened. He had his supper without having to sing for it at all!

He's sitting at my side now, making me write to you because he says I suffer from premature ejaculation and need treatment. I've never had any trouble wanking, but now I'm dead worried.

Tim (Middlesbrough)

Premature ejaculation — cumming too soon — is a very common problem. In Tony's case I can appreciate how disappointing it can be when the gun shoots at the same moment as the flash. That's just a bit too quick for anyone, but ideas of how soon is too soon vary from person to person. Some guys are happy to cum after just a few minutes while others will argue that cumming even after an hour is too fast. I imagine you are allowing yourself to get too worked up looking forward to your sessions together. How often do you wank in the intervening days between your meetings? Maybe if you were to satisfy yourself more often in this way the build up of excitement could be controlled.

In spite of my scepticism about the value of relating present behaviour to past experience, it may be useful to explore early events in your sex life which may have resulted in your present 'quick fire' problem. Sometimes there is a past history of the need for speed in situations where being discovered was a real likelihood. Sometimes when you've regularly tried to penetrate a tight hole the knob of your penis is aroused and ready to explode before you've actually got inside. Such habits, once established, can only be broken after a period of retraining.

Such retraining is similar to that encouraged for the

treatment of impotence. The idea is to concentrate not upon achieving your own climax but rather upon that of your partner. They say that it is better to give than to receive, so keep your own fly buttoned up and hang up a 'Don't Touch' notice while you do everything in your power to work on him and give him the thrill of the century. You'll be so busy working on him that your attention will be diverted from your own dick and you should be able to hold on. When his grunting and moaning lets you know that his time is nigh you can then think about preparing your own chopper for action and, with experience and a bit of luck, you'll both come off together.

The American sex therapists Masters and Johnson describe what they call the 'squeeze technique' to delay imminent orgasm. They claim that if the glans is squeezed tightly between thumb and forefinger from front to back, just as orgasm would seem to be inevitable, then the sensation will go away and the action can be prolonged. OK, this idea may work with some folk but I've found it to be singularly unsuccessful.

Another trick to prolong the arousal period and delay climax also works with some guys. After a normal orgasm the penis goes into the so-called 'refractory state' for a period of time which varies in length from person to person, and even in the same person from day to day depending upon his level of sexual excitement. It can be as short as a few minutes or as long as twenty-four to thirty-six hours. During this time no amount of restimulation will produce a second orgasm. There then follows a period of gradual recovery when further action will eventually result in climax, but it can take quite a long time. If you know when you are likely to have a sex session which you hope will be long enough to be satisfying, it may be possible, through experience, to get a rough idea of your personal refractory time. By having a wank just about that time in advance of the session then, hopefully, the session itself will take place during the period of gradual recovery and premature ejaculation will be overcome.

Two other tips: 1) a local anaesthetic cream from the pharmacist can reduce sensitivity if applied to your cock a few minutes before sex; 2) a fairly thick condom can deaden sensation.

It is probably significant that all three correspondents describe themselves as being either young or inexperienced or both. Tim says he's 'dead worried' but, setting aside all I have said about premature ejaculation there is another piece of technical jargon which is probably appropriate to all of them. They are all sexual neophytes, which means that they are sexual beginners even though they've been champing at the bit to get onto the active scene for years. Early sexual experiences, especially after a long period of anticipating 'the big day', frequently result in a very rapid climax. As time passes and a more regular pattern of sexual activity is established the novelty begins to wear off and I can almost guarantee that the early climax problem will go away. It's almost like a baby learning to control its bladder. With experience most guys learn to control the timing of their orgasm to suit their partner, making the period of arousal last until both parties decide that the time is right.

Sexual neophytes very often can't cum at all when they are with their first partners, though they have no difficulty when they wank on their own. It can be very frustrating, but such worries are almost invariably unfounded and, within a few months, the difficulty is completely overcum.

Erection Frustration

Dear Ray,

I'm forty-seven and was recently divorced. I often get the urge to wank but sometimes I just cannot get my dick hard enough to do it. It can be very frustrating to go at it for half to three-quarters of an hour and then have to give up and try again later. And when I do eventually cum I feel utterly exhausted, as if every bit of energy has been drained out of me.

The trouble is that I know I haven't been very exciting to my partners on one or two recent occasions.

When I move shortly to my own place I'd love to

strike up a friendship with a regular guy but I'm reluctant to take any step while I have this problem. I'm a rather nervous person generally. Could this be the cause? For the past two years or so I've been taking tablets prescribed to me by my GP for anxiety and relief of pain due to arthritis.

Luke (St Helens)

I think it is fair to say that a nervous guy who has been treated for two years for anxiety and then goes through a divorce shouldn't really be too surprised that he is having some wobblies over his sexual performance. Contrary to your reluctance to find a new partner before resolving your problem I suggest that this may well be the best thing that could happen to you. A firm gay relationship after years of a frustrating marriage, which was clearly not in keeping with your sexuality, is likely to do more good than anything else in helping you to relax, overcome your anxiety and establish a satisfactory pattern of sexual behaviour.

Impotence (failure to achieve an erection) must be amongst the top half-dozen topics about which I receive letters. It seems to happen at all ages and older readers should not presume, as they all too often do, that it is an inevitable consequence of the passing of the years. The conviction that one cannot achieve an erection, perhaps because of failure so often in the past, is the most counter-productive attitude to overcoming the problem. It is essential to retain a strong will and determination to succeed. Despondency and depression inevitably lead to persistence of 'the droop'.

Impotence can be caused through both physical and psychological factors and it has to be admitted that the former group are the most difficult to resolve. Impotence secondary to diabetes is one such physical cause. So, too, is Peyronie's Disease which is a degenerative condition of the spongy tissue of the cock shaft resulting in the formation of fibrous tissue which fails to stretch and thus obstructs erection. An excess of alcohol in the body, after a night out, may also make one's ardour softer!

Many men naturally awake with an erection first thing in the morning. Those who do can be reasonably confident that there is no physical cause for any impotence which they may experience later in the day. In such circumstances, when trousers, dick and spirits are all down at the same time, a psychological or emotional cause is very likely. Probably psychological impotence is the most common, but it is none the less real to the sufferer and to tell him to 'snap out of it' offers no help whatsoever.

Just as is the case with premature ejaculation, a similar retraining schedule is necessary. The longer the impotence has existed the more difficult it is to resolve the situation. To be most successful it is best to have a regular, understanding partner who has agreed to cooperate in the retraining programme. Frequent sex is better than occasional incidents with long intervening periods of abstinence.

Instead of experiencing the frustration of his own inadequacy, for the first several occasions the patient should not seek any sexual gratification for himself at all. He should not undress and neither he nor his partner should so much as even brush against his genitalia. He should concentrate totally and solely upon giving pleasure to his partner either manually or orally. In the fulfilment of time, so the text books tell us, he will begin to achieve intense personal satisfaction at having successfully brought off his lover. This secondary gratification often leads to a spontaneous erection where there wasn't one before. Then, gradually and as the retraining progresses, the partner can begin to pay more and more attention to the patient's cock. With luck, constant support and reassurance, the problem will resolve itself.

Sometimes a flagging erection can be strengthened by wearing a cockstrap at the base of the cock shaft and behind the balls. Some people have lashed out on expensive treatments involving direct injections into the penis of either Papavarine Hydrochloride or Prostaglandins. Whether or not such injections are successful seems to be very much just the luck of the draw!

A lot of work has been done on surgically inserting various

forms of 'splint' into the tissue of the penis to create an artificial, but nevertheless useful, erection. These are often very successful and highly acclaimed by those in whom they have been inserted.

Not all soft dicks are properly described as impotent. Some guys always achieve a rock solid erection, but there are others whose perfectly normal pricks have never been able to aspire to such hardness. The next two letters bring out the point.

Not Hard Enough

Dear Ray,

I'm a gay male, aged thirty, whose sexual problem involves inadequate or insufficient erections (not impotence).

I don't know where to go for help without paying enormous fees because all sex therapy clinics seem to deal only with straight couples and I am neither straight nor one of a couple.

My partners seem to judge me on the basis of a one-night stand and consequently I don't hold out much hope of a long-term relationship. I've got to the stage where the thought of disappointing myself and my partner is putting me off sex altogether. I cannot turn my erections on and off like a light switch as so many people seem able to do.

B.E. (Sheffield)

From your categorical statement that your problem is not impotence I assume that you can get an erection but that it is not hard enough to enable you to do all the things that you would like to do with it. The matter of switching erections on and off like a light switch is, I think, something of a false impression which you may have gained. It is true that

spontaneous erections often occur with very little to account
for them, and most guys, at thirty, don't need much in the
way of stimulation to bring themselves to attention, but the
idea that most of us can come up and down at will — rather
like a yo-yo — is a bit far-fetched. (Having said that, I recall
a demonstration some years ago in a New Orleans sex show
where the guy concerned came up and down at will — about
ten seconds in each direction — in rapid fire succession. It
was truly fascinating.)

Erection strengths do vary from one person to another.
Some pricks seem to be anatomically incapable of getting as
steel-hard as others. Even when they are fully roused they
have a 'lazy-lob' appearance and remain quite flexible. It
sounds to me as if this is the kind of weapon with which you
have been blessed. Have you tried a cockstrap to see if it
improves the situation?

Cumming Off Beat

Dear Ray,

Amongst the various letters which have appeared
in your column about cock size I have not seen any
reference to the following. I don't think that being big
is particularly beautiful, especially after I suffered
recently when a guy with a particularly large member
tried to screw me, but I have seen several blokes who
get what I would call a 'flaccid erection'. Although
they don't get as rock-hard as I do, they are still able
to ejaculate even though they remain quite soft.

Is this common, and why does it happen?

Tony (Midlothian)

Usually the penis is erect at the time of ejaculation but your
experiences are not all that uncommon. Provided stimulation of the nerve endings is sufficient ejaculation will occur

even when the organ is soft. This can cause penetration problems into arse or vagina.

Large penises are particularly prone to being only semi-stiff at the time of orgasm because, when full of blood, they are too heavy to stand up stiffly. The blood pressure is simply insufficient to keep them up.

Many guys find it difficult to maintain an erection while they are being fucked or finger-fucked, but massaging the prostate gland through the wall of the rectum often causes semen to be milked out in large quantities although the penis remains totally soft. You may have experienced the same thing yourself on the toilet when passing a large mass of faeces.

I remember once being given a hand-made, fur-lined, leather jock strap which I was wearing for the first time on a coach journey to London. Suddenly with neither preliminary warning nor an erection I ejaculated spontaneously and had to put up with a right sticky mess for the best part of 100 miles along the M4.

Cock-a-Leakie!

Dear Ray,

I expect you'll think that my problem is rather 'wet'. Well, it is really. You see, every time I go for a piss my dick drips for a long time after the stream has stopped flowing. I have to stand at the loo for several minutes until it has finished or else I wet myself if I put it away too soon.

I'm fifty-nine and I've led a very active sex life ever since I was about thirteen. I still get a hard-on, no sweat, whenever I need one and I live with a boy-friend who is much younger than I am and makes very heavy demands upon me. We have a routine which involves sex three times a day... before we get up in the morning, when we get home from work in the early evening and again when we go to bed before going to sleep. I never fail to ejaculate and sometimes that annoys him intensely because, though he is thirty years younger, he sometimes can't make it.

I was circumcised about eighteen months ago for no other reason than that I fancied the idea. My boyfriend was cut at the same time, again for no special reason.

My dripping problem seems to have commenced round about the time I was circumcised. Do you think that operation was to blame or do you think it has something to do with the frequency with which I have my rocks off.

Naughton (Plymouth)

Your problem has nothing to do with either the frequency of your sexual escapades or the fact that you've been up for the chop. It's just a sign of the times. I'm afraid that the first hint of the autumn of life is upon you. Your prostate gland at the neck of your bladder is getting bigger, as it often does in guys of your age, and is causing an obstruction to the urine flow. As the enlargement advances you may find it more difficult to start to pass urine and the power of the stream will diminish. Perhaps you'll also feel the need to go more frequently and to get up in the night. Such enlargement is usually harmless but is sometimes malignant so if it progresses rapidly or if there is also the appearance of any blood in your urine you should go to your doctor for a full investigation.

It may be that you will eventually need to have the gland removed surgically. If that becomes necessary it is no longer the rather bloody operation it once was.

Nowadays the usual method is known as a 'transurethral resection of the prostate'. It involves passing an instrument called a cystoscope along the tube of your penis. This instrument is like a telescope with a light at the end and when the surgeon looks through it he can see what is going on inside. He can then pass a a further instrument along the cystoscope and with this he can snip away at the prostate until he cuts it out. The main bleeding points can then be electrically cauterised and stopped.

The alternative 'supra-pubic' operation involves an incision into the abdomen above the pubic bone. The surgeon then makes his way down through the tissues until he finds the gland and cuts it out with a scalpel.

Naturally things are a bit sore for a week or two but gradually they settle down. At first it is a bit difficult to hold one's urine but control is soon re-established. Sexually, the power of erection should not be affected, although some men do experience difficulties for a varying lengths of time. Nor should the ability to achieve an orgasm be impaired, and some folk resume sexual activities about five to six weeks after surgery. There is one major difference, though. Post-prostatectomy the ability to ejaculate semen is almost invariably lost. The orgasm is dry, or very nearly so. This is because it was the prostate gland which produced more than 90 per cent of the total volume of semen. The internal scarring which is inevitably left at the site of the gland blocks off the ducts which carried the remaining contents of the spunk and so, even that disappears. Maybe the pre-cum juices, which are produced by small glands in the urethra itself, will continue to flow.

Pee Problem

Dear Ray,

After a free and unattached bachelor life until the age of fifty-four, during which I enjoyed a sufficient but certainly not an excessive sex-life made up mainly of one-night stands, I have been living with the same guy for the past two years. We are both very much in love. He is a divorcee who was married for thirty years and so has a lot more experience of regular sexual activity than I have, albeit mainly heterosexual hitherto.

Don't ask me why it has happened this way, but we have developed our own pattern of lovemaking which involves long periods of kissing and cuddling and genital stimulation but rarely actually going so far as orgasm. We like to keep ourselves 'on the boil' — just one pull short of cumming — often for a couple of hours or more. After such a long time it often happens that our erections spontaneously subside and that's that! We roll over and go to sleep, feeling very satisfied and contented.

My problem is that I usually reawake in about half an hour with an intense desire to pee but when I go to the loo the flow takes ages to start and only dribbles so that it may take ten minutes or more to empty my bladder. What's more my balls can be tender most of the following day and I get a vague sort of ache in my lower abdomen and deep down somewhere behind the root of my cock. It can be quite unpleasant.

My partner, who is actually a year older than I am, never experiences these problems. Do you think it is because he has had a more regular sex-life than I have?

Nick (Accrington)

Although I believe that a regular and full sex life should form a key part of a healthy lifestyle I do not think the relative infrequency and irregularity of your one-night stands prior to settling down with your lover has anything to do with your symptoms.

Prolonged sexual activity causes very considerable engorgement of the prostate gland which lies at the neck of your bladder surrounding the urethra. The gland increases very substantially in size since it produces most of the fluid of your semen. If you don't ejaculate, this fluid is not released and the engorgement persists for several hours, causing the discomforting ache which you describe. It is not uncommon for men of your age to develop an enlarged prostate gland as a simple feature of the aging process and this can considerably obstruct the urinary flow. Because the bladder doesn't empty completely there is a strong urge to pass urine more frequently but the stream is very weak.

I suspect that your prostate is already showing signs of middle-age size increase and, though this isn't sufficient yet to cause any noticeable problems under normal circumstances, when you get the added engorgement of prolonged sexual arousal that's when your difficulties begin.

Spontaneously going 'off the boil' after a long period of sexual arousal without orgasm is quite natural. If your symptoms become too much to cope with I suggest that they are likely to be very much eased if you allow yourself to cum before the session peters out.

Beautiful Dreamer

Dear Ray,
Please will you write to my mum and tell her that wet dreams are normal.

I cum in my sleep two or three times a week after a wildly exciting gay orientated dream. It must happen quite shortly before I wake up because the sheets are still wet when my mother makes my bed after I've gone to work.

Night after night she gives me hell about it when I get home and calls me a filthy homosexual pervert.

The irony of the situation is that I haven't had a regular boyfriend for months and I've never been a wanker — well, not very often, anyway.

Kim (Hartlepool)

No, I'm sorry but I can't start writing to your mother out of the blue, but I have sent you a personal reply which you can show her if you wish.

You are quite right that wet dreams are a natural phenomenon, especially in virile young guys, and they often do occur shortly before waking during relatively light REM sleep. (REM stands for 'rapid eye movement'. It has been noted that during light sleep the eyes move to and fro rapidly and it is at this time that most dreaming occurs.)

The frequency of your dreams is quite probably due to the fact that you don't wank very often. If you 'drained yourself' daily the reservoir of unejaculated semen wouldn't overflow. Wet dreams are nothing more than a simple safety valve.

Still Dreaming

Dear Ray,

I was interested in the letter from Kim of Hartlepool who wanted you to explain to his mum that wet dreams are normal because she got angry with him about his spunk-stained sheets in the morning.

I think my problem is even more embarrassing. I'm forty-five and I live with a great guy who is only twenty-one. We have a really wonderful and loving sex life and sometimes climax two or three times during the night. However, there are many nights when we don't have any sex at all. We just go to bed, snuggle up together and sleep. Maybe it's because we are particularly tired after a late party or maybe we just don't feel like it. There's nothing wrong in that, is there?

It's on the nights when nothing happens that I regularly have a wet dream and, because we are so closely embraced I invariably cum all over his tummy or his back. He doesn't mind at all when we've been making love together but he gets really upset when he wakes up to find himself all covered in spunk without having shared in the action. He calls me all the names under the sun and says I'm dirty and disgusting. He makes me feel really guilty though I know there is nothing I can do about it. What makes it even worse is that when I have these wet dreams I always dream about having sex with a stranger — never with my lover who is in bed beside me. Since it always happens on the nights when we don't feel like having sex together, it's no good telling me that the best cure would be to have a wank before going to sleep. I'm no good at forcing myself when I'm not in the mood.

Leslie (Dumbarton)

As you say, you have a problem! In the excitement of sexual arousal your boyfriend is quite happy to be 'shot upon'. But, even though he probably understands the spontaneity of your wet dreams and the lack of control that you have over them, he is upset at being plastered with spunk when he isn't excited. Perhaps it is at moments like that when he becomes more acutely aware of the twenty-four year age gap between you. It is, after all, just a little unusual for a man of your age to continue to have wet dreams with such regularity. You can't blame him if fate dictates that he should feel that way any more than you can blame yourself for having uncontrollable night emissions. It simply reflects the sensibilities of his personality and your fortunate virility.

You may have to resort to the paradoxical situation of wearing a condom all night on the occasions when you aren't going to have sex, or you may have to sleep in a pair of snug-fitting briefs to hold a hanky as a 'catcher pad'. I certainly think it would be better to let nature take its course and try to catch it in some way rather than resort to some medication, like the use of sleeping pills, in the hope that you will stop it from happening.

I really hesitate to try to speculate on why your dreams should be associated with a stranger rather than your partner. Maybe it is because in your conscious state you know that it upsets your boyfriend so, in your sleep, you transfer the dream to some other individual rather than cause distress to the one you love. But don't quote me on that!

No, of course there is nothing wrong in even the closest of lovers quite often having nights when they sleep together without having sex and without having to analyse why not.

Pain In The Arse

Dear Ray,

Because I love my boyfriend very much I do my best to conceal the fact that when he fucks me it is excruciatingly painful. The problem is that his cock is very thick — almost six inches in circumference. If I enjoyed the pain I suppose I would be a masochist, but I most definitely do not.

On the other hand, after the act is over and I am lying in his arms, I have a great feeling of euphoria which I put down to the pleasure which I have so obviously given to him.

Can you give me any advice on how I can mitigate this dreadful pain so that, hopefully, I can enjoy the act and not suffer so much?

Benny (Plymouth)

Human intellectual sophistication and ingenuity have managed, in some degree, to eliminate pain, or to learn to endure and live with it, or, as in the case of the masochist, even to enjoy it. Nevertheless, we should never forget that Nature's intention is that we should recognise pain as an indication that something is wrong. If it is 'excruciatingly painful' when someone fucks you, as opposed to the tolerable level of discomfort which many of us expect under those circumstances, heed the warning. It is quite likely that muscles, other organs and tissues are being endangered. Superficial anal abrasions may cause bleeding and be an entry point for infection. Deeper muscle damage to the anal sphincter could lead to incontinence with the passage of time. The wall of the rectum might be bruised, or even perforated, and deeper injury to the prostate or bladder is always a remote possibility. Powerful pain-killing drugs may remove the agony but they certainly wouldn't eliminate the risk.

The key to pain-free anal intercourse lies in the ability to relax the anal sphincter together with plenty of lubrication. Some guys are never able to relax sufficiently and have to accept the fact. Others can train themselves through extended periods of very loving and gentle foreplay until all their inhibitions are relieved. A very high state of arousal then overcomes the tension and fear which leads to an involuntary clenching of the anus.

One way of physically encouraging the anus to learn to relax is to lie on one's back in a hot bath with one's feet up on the edge on either side of the taps. Dildoes of graduated sizes (eg. candles, carrots, courgettes) and well-lubricated with a non-water-soluble substance such as Vaseline, can be gradually inserted and removed (whatever you do, don't let go!) until easy entry is achieved. However, this kind of training may take very many sessions and I can't emphasise strongly enough that extreme care should be taken never to use excessive force.

You are another one of my anonymous correspondents. I wish we could engage in personal correspondence because I always fear that some readers will act upon my advice in circumstances where it may be dangerous (eg. someone with piles may be caused to haemorrhage). Before anyone attempts such stretching exercises they should contact me to discuss their personal circumstances.

Hurt Like Hell

Dear Ray,
      John fucked me for the first time in my life a few days ago. He is only average size and I thought it

would be easy but it hurt like hell. Other guys seem to enjoy being fucked and I was really looking forward to it, but now I'm afraid to try it again ·

Terry (Slough)

The human arse is normally set tight shut against being opened by pressure from the outside and it is very often quite a painful experience being fucked for the first time because you are tense and tight with anticipation. You have to learn to relax the anal muscle ring and that's a trick which only comes with practice. Some guys never learn how. They always hold themselves too tight so being fucked is always uncomfortable for them. Others learn to relax very quickly and soon come to enjoy the sensation of having their prostate massaged from inside through the rectum wall.

Try it this way. Get John to lie on his back on the bed or on the floor with his cock sticking vertically upwards and a pillow beneath his buttocks to raise him slightly. Next, squat astride him either facing his feet or his head according to your preference. Make sure his cock is well lubricated (and wearing a condom of course!) and lower yourself down onto him, gripping his weapon as you do so, so that you can gently guide it in. This way you are completely in control of the rate and angle of penetration and you can stop whenever you want to. You'll gradually learn the knack and be able to move on to other positions in which John takes a more active role.

A Pain In The Balls

Dear Ray,

I am writing to ask you about something which seems to happen a lot judging by scenes on the television — I'm talking about a man having his testicles squeezed.

What is the chance of permanent damage being done? Can your reproductive prospects be really knocked out by the practice? Can nerve and tissue damage ruin one's sex life?

I'm asking because it happened to me some time ago. What should I do about it? See my GP? See a urologist in hospital? Put on some cream or spray?

Raymond (Maidstone)

Your question begs an 'it all depends' answer. Completely crushing the testicles to pulp (ouch!) could be as destructive as castration and was the method used in the East to create the eunuchs so prized as slaves. However the squeezing hich occurs during average levels of sexual horseplay or S & M sessions rarely causes any permanent harm.

Our testicles are actually very resilient to crush injury though the short-term pain can be quite excruciating. This intense pain, and even the threat of it when someone makes a grab at you, is Nature's way of protecting mankind's most vital function — his ability to reproduce himself. Every other bodily function is subservient to the principal drive to preserve and propagate our species. Even those of us who are gay, with no intention of having children, have the same self-preservation instincts.

In spite of what happened to you, unless you have chronic pain or are aware that your sexual ability has suffered, it is most unlikely that any serious harm befell you.

Tactile Testicular Tantrum!

Dear Ray,

I was feeling my testicles the other day while I was having a wank and I found a kind of a lump behind the right one. 'Christ', I thought to myself , 'I've got cancer.' Honestly I did a real 'wobbly' and couldn't get to my GP quick enough.

I sure was relieved when he told me I was feeling the normal epididymis (see, I've got all the jargon!) which is the place where all the tubules carrying the sperm from the testicles join up together to form the vas deferens which carries the semen away from the bollock towards the outside. (I used the word 'bollock' to show I'm not always snooty and academic, and, anyway, 'bollock' has a lovely ring to it!)

The GP gave me a leaflet on 'Self-Examination of the Testicles' which he says all men should do regularly, like women are supposed to self-examine their own breasts, to identify early cancers. Is this a new thing? I've never heard it referred to before.

'Adie' (Northwich)

I thought it was a 'bullock', not a 'bollock', that had a ring to it, but, I agree, it is a word that rolls rather nicely over the tongue.

Although some doctors now advocate regular testicular self-examination I have some reservations because, as you discovered, unless you know exactly what you are feeling, you can be easily misled, and worried by, perfectly normal knots and lumps which you detect. Personally I believe that if you want someone to feel your balls you should leave it to the professionals... Come up and see me sometime!

If you do decide to be a testicular self-examiner, do it regularly, once a month, so that you become fully accustomed to the normal feel of the contents of your scrotum (bollock bag!). Then you'll notice any lumps or changes in weight or size when they occur and will be sensibly alerted to seek help. The regular touch will save the terror tantrums.

Teenage Tits

Dear Ray,

I'm terrified. I'm twenty-one but I've been having it off with a kid of fifteen. I know it's against the law and that's why I'm writing completely anonymously.

The boy seems perfectly healthy except that he's complaining that both his breast nipples are getting bigger and hurting him. He says it's probably my fault for fucking him and he's going to tell his GP what's been happening.

What can I do?

Anon. (Sheffield)

What the boy does with regard to telling his GP is entirely up to him. No way am I going to get involved in even suggesting, in public, ways of covering up illegal sex acts with minors. That would make me an 'accessory after the fact'.

However, on the strictly medical issue, my guess is that the boy concerned is experiencing the perfectly ordinary condition called 'Gynaecomasty of Puberty'. When the surge of sex hormones enters the bloodstream at puberty it is very common for a boy's nipples and breasts to swell up — sometimes they even discharge a little milky fluid. It can be very embarrassing and there is sometimes some tenderness, but it usually settles down in a year or two. It isn't anything to do with whatever you've been up to with him. That's completely irrelevant.

Post-Ejaculatory Depression

Dear Ray,

Please help me with my very distressing problem.

I'm a young man who began masturbating around puberty. My father once caught me at it but was most

understanding and supportive so I have no reason to
feel guilty about it. The urge to wank comes over me
three or four times a week and is very compelling, but
as soon as I cum I feel dirty, ashamed and depressed
and vow that I'll never do it again. I really hate
myself.

I have a lover and the reaction isn't nearly so bad
when I'm with him. He seems to uplift my spirits and
the after-effects of cumming when I'm with him are
really quite enjoyable as we cuddle up together.

Simon (Truro)

Masturbation is Nature's completely normal, and very important, sexual safety outlet and training technique. It is not
some inferior alternative to partnered sex. Quite often,
though, young people get it into their heads that they are
being disloyal to present, or even future, lovers if they toss
themselves off. Perhaps they believe it implies that their
lovers aren't satisfying them. Subconsciously, in spite of
reassurances that it is a right and proper thing to do and
should, in fact, be encouraged, they still feel guilty and worry
about it. This can lead to the sort of depression which you
describe. It can be very intense in some people and may even
lead to suicide. I remember one such very tragic incident
dating back to my student days.

You are silly to make a vow that you will never wank again
because you know jolly well that you will and you only
undermine your own ego and make things worse.

The sexual cycle involves three phases — excitation, orgasm and resolution. The post-orgasm resolution phase is
very vulnerable to all sorts of guilts and depressions. It is an
important phase which many guys ignore. As soon as they've
cum they put their cock away and get on with living. But if it
is used for a period of conscious relaxation, beautiful thoughts
and fantasies, and gentle continued stimulation until all the
sensation has died away, it can be a very rewarding experi-

ence. Make the most of it when you are on your own, as well as when you are with your partner, and I'm sure you'll soon resolve your problem.

No-Slip Lubrication

Dear Ray,
Please can you give some general advice on sexual lubricants? We hear a lot about oil-based and water-soluble lubricants and those which contain anti-HIV additives. I'm sure some helpful hints on what's what would be very valuable.

Iain (Glasgow)

As you rightly say, there are two regular kinds of sexual lubricants — water-based and oil-based. The commonest water- soluble lubricant (not to be seriously recommended) is spit and the most popular commercial product is KY jelly. The oil-based lubricants are essentially of three kinds — mineral oils such as petroleum jelly (Vaseline) or baby oil, vegetable oils such as corn oil or grapeseed oil, and animal fats such as butter or lard.

Latex, the stuff from which condoms are made, easily disintegrates especially under the influence of mineral oils and so a water-soluble lubricant is really essential when you use a condom for a fuck. Many condoms already have a safe lubricant added during manufacture. Don't forget to check whether this contains the spermicide Nonoxinol 9 if you know that you are allergic to it.

I've already described the problem of water-based lubricants drying out and leading to friction burns, so when the sexual action doesn't involve any threat to latex an oil-based lubricant is preferable. Castrol GTX would work but, when you are oiling your balls rather than your ball-bearings, something a little more refined is called for. I'm very much into some of the light, aromatic oils used in massage work — eg. grapeseed oils. While hardly a gastronomic delight they are more acceptable than, say, petroleum jelly to a dedicated cock-sucker like me. However, if you want to lubricate dildoes or if you are up to magnificent mischief in a bath or shower these light oils are washed off very quickly and that's when something more robust like Vaseline or butter (for the oralist again) comes into its own.

Just as a quick warning, remember if your sexual foreplay involves lubricated finger-fucking or dildo work use a water-soluble lubricant if you intend moving onto latex-protected intercourse. If there is any residual oil-based lubricant in your rectum you could still damage the condom.

Baby oil/lotion and several of the oil-based skin conditioning creams and lotions like Vaseline Intensive Care (mineral) or Christie's Lanolin (animal) are excellent for general cock care. Those of us who don't let the grass grow under our foreskins, in that we use our endowment with both frequency and vigour, need to keep the skin supple and soft.

Water Sports — Or Else

Dear Ray,

I had been very lonely for several months after my last affair walked out on me. Then I found this magic new guy as beautiful as ever you did see. We love each other more than any words can describe. He sold up his flat and moved in with me about six weeks ago and, to begin with, everything was wonderful. Now I have a problem.

We are both into rubberwear — pants, vests, etc. — and we usually cum simply by cuddling and body rubbing when we are dressed up in all our gear. Often we don't actually see each other's cock at all during a session and the feeling of our form-fitting rubber pants full of spunk is really brill. But I'm not so sure about his latest demands. He wants to move into water sports and is particularly determined to make me drink his piss straight down my throat from his cock. I don't know why he seems to have become suddenly so obsessed with the idea but he is threatening that it is a make or break issue between us. I don't know whether drinking urine would be dangerous but, in any case, I don't fancy it at all — yet I don't want to lose him.

Dameon (Cleveland)

While the dangers of piss drinking are not very great it would be irresponsible of me to encourage such activities because infections can sometimes be transmitted in this way. However, if you don't fancy the idea, I don't think you should agree simply to satisfy your boyfriend because of your love for him. That affection is bound to be undermined if he persists in forcing you to do something against your will.

Remember that you already hold the upper hand to some extent. He has sold up his flat to move in with you. If the relationship is broken it will be he who is homeless, not you. What's more, if he insists on going through with his ideas, regardless of your wishes, you have to ask yourself whether he is worthy of the love which you currently feel for him. True mutual love is a give and take experience on both sides and he should be more sensitive to your wishes if his love for you is as genuine as he professes it to be.

You enjoy slopping around in your spunk-filled rubber pants and I suspect that you would probably get quite a thrill out of some piss play, short of drinking the stuff, if you were to experiment. Why not try to agree at least to explore some sort of half-way compromise? There has to be a first time for everything and, who knows, it may turn out to be the best thing since gin and tonic!

I'm In The Nude For Love!

Dear Ray,

I suppose it's all to do with the narrow upbringing I had in a strict Welsh non-conformist background, but I simply can't let anyone see me in the nude. It took me a hell of a long time to come to terms with the fact that I'm gay and my early sexual experiences were very definitely just snogging and groping sessions without ever allowing my trousers to be unzipped. I was terrified of anyone else seeing or, worse still, touching my cock.

Then I met a very insistent boyfriend and we just had to go all the way. Even so, I was petrified and insisted on the room being in pitch darkness with everything happening under the sheets by feel only. I stubbornly kept my pyjamas on all night.

Nowadays I'm something of a heathen. I haven't been to chapel for years and I have quite a lively sex life, but the old inhibitions linger on. I still go to all sorts of subterfuges to get into bed without my partner actually seeing my cock — which is silly because I'm thick and seven inches so I've nothing to be ashamed of — and I insist on showering before and afterwards in total privacy even though my partner may ask to come into the cubicle with me for a little cuddle under the spray.

To be honest, I don't really like seeing my partners naked either and tend to blush and look the other way if they undress or parade their equipment in front of me.

What's the answer?

Jess (Aberystwyth)

Although you say you now enjoy a lively sex life, your inhibitions about nudity clearly reveal that you still have some pretty deep-seated guilty feelings about sex. You are obviously quite well equipped and it is a pity that you are depriving your partners of the added turn-on of seeing what you can offer them. Remember that the visual attraction of seeing something beautiful is an important element in love making.

There isn't an easy way of overcoming your embarrassment. It probably means revealing more and more of yourself in stages just in the same way as you gradually progressed from the 'snogging and groping' stage to the full sexual union.

You may find it easier to bare all in the first instance in a strictly non-sexual environment — eg. the changing room of your local swimming bath — but choose a time when you aren't going to be frightened off by too many other bathers. Or maybe you could go along with a friend for company to a sauna. The fact that you've been able to talk about it to me is, in itself, part of the battle. You've brought your thoughts into the open. Now all you have to do is summon the courage to bring your dick into the open as well.

I'm reminded of the parody of the old popular song 'I'm in the "Nude" for Love!'

●●●

If this chapter has provided a little bedtime reading and you are now about to turn over and gaze dreamily into the eyes of your lover whose head is on the pillow next to you, perhaps now is the time to forget all the woes which do betide us and croon into his ear those very words: 'I'm in the Mood for Love.'

9

ENCORE!

Well, that's it really. There's not much more to write. If you've cum along with me all this way you'll realise what a potpourri of my correspondence this has been. I was never a particularly tidy individual and I've found it very hard to allocate all the letters precisely into the right chapter. As I've been reading over the manuscript I've asked myself 'Why did I put that letter there?' on many occasions, but then I've thought 'Why not?' and pressed on regardless.

However, there are some letters which just don't seem to fit in anywhere. So, as a sort of encore (to avoid the use of that filing clerk's nightmare word 'miscellaneous'), here are a few, together with some extracts, which show what I mean.

Versatile

Dear Ray,

My cock gets all sticky when horny,
The result of its wanting to play.
But there are times when it really is naughty,
'Cos it stands up at odd times of the day.

I don't mind when it's out in the sunshine,
And I'm certainly tolerant at night.
But a messy wet patch on my crotchline
Is revealing to all of my plight.

John (Kidderminster)

To which I replied ....

> Your poem has clutched at my heartstring,
> But, alas, I can't weep many tears.
> Though your dewdrops of love need restraining
> The problem is less than your fears.
>
> To the many similarly afflicted
> The answer has easily been had.
> The stains of their juice are restricted
> By wearing a rolled hanky pad.

Sweet And Sour

Dear Ray,
    How is it that some people's spunk is really salty to taste and others' is quite sweet? I find that young men tend to be sweeter than older men, some of whom are like brine. Is there any salt at all in spunk?

'The Yorkshire Zipper'

No book of mine could possibly be complete without a contribution from an anonymous 'friend' of mine who has been writing to me from Yorkshire for many years, always using a different pen name but never hiding the hallmarks which show him to be the same man. I have never been able to reply to him, which is a pity because he has often asked most interesting questions and I would have loved to have made personal contact.

Yes, there is quite a lot of sodium, which imparts the salty taste, in spunk. There is no doubt that the flavour does vary from person to person but I don't think that it has anything to do with age. I remember an Asian friend of mine whose semen invariably tasted of curry and it is said that heavy smokers impart a smoky flavour to their cum. I have no doubt that the differences are due to minor variations in the mix of the principal constituents of semen, but I can't imagine anyone embarking on expensive research relating chemical formulation to flavour.

Colour TV

Dear Ray,
    I've had this marvellous fun idea for my Christmas party orgy. We all turn up in drag and, because we've all taken special pills beforehand, when we have sex we all shoot spunk of different colours. The only trouble is I don't know what pills to take. Can you advise me?

Bill (London)

You cannot be serious! Surely your party would be more suitable for April Fool's Day?

Banana Boy

Dear Ray,
    I'm a real 'tight arse' so my lover told me to loosen up by exercising my anus with a banana. It was too thick so I peeled it and the bloody thing broke off inside. What a way to feed the animals!

Kenny (Telford)

Well, at least you've got the bananas. All you need now is for your lover to send the 'cream' up after them.

Condom Disposal

Dear Ray,

My boyfriend and I use condoms religiously. After withdrawal we tie a knot in the end and throw them down the toilet but, unfortunately, even though they are wrapped in tissues, they often contain enough air to keep them afloat and they fail to flush away. This has caused embarrassment in the household.

Ricky (Cardiff)

Don't tie a knot in the condom. Fill it with water under the tap and then drop it like a bomb down the toilet pan while the latter is in full flush. You'll find it disappears with no bother at all. (Until it reaches the sewage works — Ed.)

Fellating Fido

Dear Ray,

My neighbour's dog is a compulsive cock-licker. If I leave the door open it comes into the house and follows me to the toilet and as soon as I expose myself it's a case of 'lick, lick, slurp, slurp' as if it's licking an ice lolly. It really puts me off pissing.

Likewise, if I change prior to going out, as soon as I remove my jeans it starts its licking as if mine was the last cock on earth.

It quite clearly gets aroused, but it makes no attempt to mount me — thank God! Do you think the dog has been doctored to reduce its urge to mount and is all this cock licking harmful in any way — to me, I mean, not the dog?

Archie (Bristol)

Variations of this theme land on my desk two or three times every year involving cats, dogs and even sheep. I suspect that the animal is attracted by the smell of the smegma which is the sticky lubricant under your foreskin and doubt whether it sees any sexual connotation whatsoever in what it is doing. I'm sure you were taken aback the first time it happened but I suggest you were amused and now possibly even encourage it for a laugh... Go on, admit it!

You ask whether the dog has been doctored. Find out for yourself by looking for its balls, and as for whether the habit is likely to prove harmful, well, tell the dog to 'suck it and see'!

Out In The Sun

Dear Ray,

After a wet summer, during which those of us who are gay naturists have had little chance to bare our bollocks to the breeze and brown our bums on the beaches, I'm planning an autumn sunbathing holiday on the shores of the Mediterranean and I think I'll hire a sunbed for a couple of weeks before I go. There has been so much talk of sunlight causing skin cancers I thought I'd seek your views first.

Richard (Liverpool)

When we expose our lily-white skin to the vicious ultra-violet rays of the sun or sunbed we can burn very easily, and readily go down with the sickness and headaches of sunstroke. There is also evidence to suggest that small pigmented skin moles can occasionally become cancerous under the influence of too much sunshine. However, don't get things out of perspective. The cancer risk is very rare and is no greater to your cock and bollocks than any other exposed part of your body. Be sensible. Use a high filter cream or lotion in the early days and don't stay out for longer than a half hour or so to begin with.

Short periods on the sunbed before you go will help to toughen your skin and prepare you for the beaches ahead. Remember that, because of reflected rays from the water, the light is much stronger on the sands than you realise. If you lose a lot of fluid through perspiration don't forget to drink plenty of soft drinks in preference to beer and keep up your salt intake to reduce the risk of sunstroke.

The Plot Thickens

Dear Ray,

I have written several modestly successful crime novels and am currently engaged on a gay murder story. I need to know whether a person's erection would be maintained should he die suddenly when he's got a hard-on. I would also like to know whether there is any way that semen could be extracted from a corpse shortly after death.

Anon. (Guildford)

Because of the complete collapse of blood pressure at the time of death any erection at that moment would rapidly disappear. Loss of erection may be delayed for a few minutes only if the victim were to be wearing a tight cockstrap at the time.

It is a fairly well known phenomenon that strangulation as a cause of death is sometimes associated with a spontaneous ejaculation (I don't know why) but I cannot think that it would be possible to produce semen from a corpse. Mind you, I've never tried!

Children In Need

Dear Ray,

    At our local gay club we were sponsored to produce half a litre of spunk for Children In Need. Several of us had a hell of a lot of wanking to do. We raised £431 but could hardly tell the BBC how we had collected the money. I think the lads deserve a mention though, don't you?

                         Stephen (Not-letting-on)

And so say all of us... Congratulations!

Monkey Business

Dear Ray,

    On a recent visit to the zoo I saw one of the apes tossing himself off. He didn't seem the least abashed or ashamed so why should mankind get so uptight about it?

                         Angus (West Lothian)

Well may you ask!

Black And Blue Blues

Dear Ray,

    Whenever I have a session with my boyfriend I seem to end up with masses of black love-bites on my neck although I'm not really conscious of him biting me at the time.

I'm thirty-five and most men of my age don't seem to be afflicted in the same way — that seems to be the preserve of the teenagers at my work who are rather proud to display their love-bites as if they are some kind of status symbol.

I find them very unsightly and they take a long time to go away. Any ideas?

Fred (Newcastle)

I'm afraid that bruises are bruises, no matter how old you are, and you just have to be patient until they go away, or more careful when you're necking. Teenagers tend to be more passionate in love-making, which is probably why they seem to get bitten more often, but the status symbol element is quite genuine. It's a way of showing the world that you are sexually active and separates the men from the boys.

●●●

And now my race is run. In presenting 'What's Wrong with my Willy?' to you I bow low in submission and leave you with this final letter...

How Now — Kow-Tow

Dear Ray,

We have all heard of people 'kow-towing' to their superiors in a demonstrative act of submission. In the gay world 'slaves' kow-tow to their 'masters' every day. I have researched the background to this ancient Chinese gesture which dates back centuries to the early Ming Dynasty. It represents the ultimate obeisance when a man folds his body in the full bow from the waist as an acknowledgement that he has relinquished rank, uniform, name, family — everything he knows or owns is completely negated. It is a most solemn practice, in every sense a rebirth, a new beginning. It does not correspond to a salute or a handshake and it cannot be undertaken without serious study. It is sacred.

In the full kow-tow the man stands naked before his overlord. His head and shoulders curl slowly forward until his mouth draws in the hardening penis. He is at one with himself — kow-towing to his own soul.

In the British Museum (where else?) there is a vase and also a print of a mandarin on a high plinth observing a naked man (in head dress only) actually in the kow-tow position. One hand is holding his organ while the other is behind the back.

The idea of self-fellatio (sucking oneself off) fascinates me. Do you know of anyone who can actually do it?

Chris (Bedford)

I confess a little confusion as to whether your description of the 'ultimate obeisance' involves the 'kow- tower' in sucking his own cock or that of the 'kow-towee'. I can't vouch for the exhibits in the British Museum but I read somewhere that self-fellatio is apparently possible by about 4 per cent of gay men — surprise, surprise! I've never seen it done in the flesh, but it has been depicted often enough in gay videos.

Where the medical input is in this letter defeats me, but one of my other correspondents has written to me that he sees my Agony Column as 'a human letterbox where gays can feel free to pour out obsessions, problems, doubts, and occasional fantasies'. He adds, 'It only takes one person to be on the receiving end to lighten the darkness'.

With that kind of compliment I guess that the above letter must be legitimate. I shall be happy to continue to receive readers' letters for possible publication in HIM Magazine (under a pseudonym and with a changed location to preserve confidentiality) and will do my best to reply personally if a stamped, self-addressed envelope is included. The address is: Dr Ray Hamble, c/o HIM Magazine, 283 Camden High St., London, NW1 7BX.

GMP books can be ordered from any bookshop in the UK,
and from specialised bookshops overseas.
If you prefer to order by mail, a comprehensive mail-order
catalogue is available on request, from:

GMP Publishers Ltd (GB),
P O Box 247, London N17 9QR.

In North America order from Alyson Publications Inc.,
40 Plympton St, Boston, MA 02118, USA.

In Australia order from Bulldog Books,
P O Box 155, Broadway, NSW 2007, Australia.

Name and Address in block letters please:

Name _____

Address _____

_____

_____